Contents

WWW.[   ]PUBLISHERS.COM
P9-DIG-239

KALAMAZOO VALLEY
COMMUNITY COLLEGE
LIBRARY
WITHDRAWN

Contents

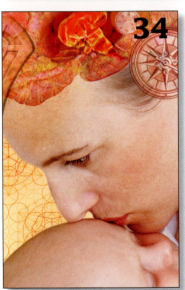

Contents

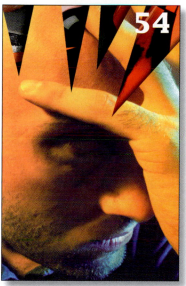

Contents

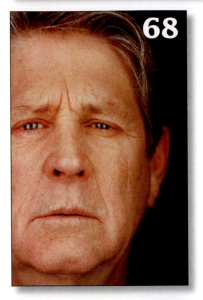

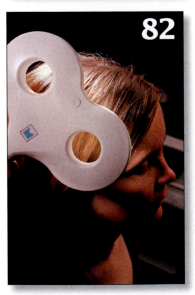

Contents

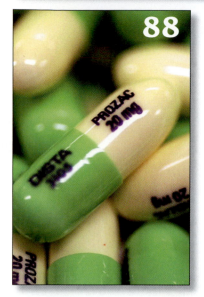
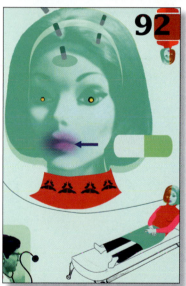

Informing the ADHD Debate

The latest neurological research has injected much needed objectivity into the disagreement over how best to treat children with attention-deficit disorders

By Aribert Rothenberger and Tobias Banaschewski

From the moment Julia entered first grade, she appeared to spend most of her time daydreaming. She needed more time to complete assignments than the other children did. As she moved through elementary school, her test scores deteriorated. She felt increasingly unable to do her homework or follow the teacher's instructions in class. She made few real friends and said her teachers got on her nerves. She complained that her par-

ents pressured her all day long and that nothing she did was right.

Julia was actually very friendly and talkative, but a lack of self-control made others feel uneasy around her. By age 14, she found that concentrating on assignments seemed impossible. She constantly lost her belongings. Neuropsychological exams showed Julia was of average intelligence but repeatedly interrupted the tests. She was easily distracted and seemed to expect failure in everything she did. So she just gave up. Ultimately Julia was diagnosed with attention-deficit hyperactivity disorder (ADHD) and was treated with methylphenidate, one of the standard drugs for her condition. The medication helped Julia organize her life and tackle her schoolwork more readily. She says she now feels better and is much more self-confident.

Julia's symptoms constitute just one profile of a child with ADHD. Other girls and boys exhibit similar yet varied traits, and whereas medication has helped in many cases, for just as many it provides no relief. With the number of cases increasing every year, debate over basic questions has heightened: Is ADHD overdiagnosed? Do drugs offer better treatment than behavior modification? Recent progress in understanding how brain activity differs in ADHD children is suggesting answers.

What Causes ADHD?

ADHD is diagnosed in 2 to 5 percent of children between the ages 6 and 16; approximately 80 percent are boys. The typical symptoms of dis-

tractibility, hyperactivity and agitation occur at all ages, even in adults who have the condition, but with considerable disparity. Children often seem forgetful or impatient, tend to disturb others and have a hard time observing limits. Poor impulse control manifests itself in rash decision making, silly antics and rapid mood swings. The child acts before thinking. And yet ADHD children often behave perfectly normally in new situations, particularly those of short duration that involve direct contact with individuals or are pleasurable or exciting, like watching TV or playing games.

Precursor behaviors such as a difficult temperament or sleep and appetite disorders have often been found in children younger than three who were later diagnosed with ADHD, but no definitive diagnosis can be made in those first three years. Physical restlessness often diminishes in teenagers, but attention failure continues and can often become associated with aggressive or antisocial behavior and emotional problems, as well as a tendency toward drug abuse. Symptoms persist into adulthood in 30 to 50 percent of cases.

Longitudinal epidemiological studies demonstrate that ADHD is no more common today than in the past. The apparent statistical rise in the number of cases may be explained by increased public awareness and improved diagnosis. The condition can now be reliably identified according to a set of characteristics that differentiate it from age-appropriate behavior. Nevertheless, debates about overdiagnosis, as well as preferred treatments, are sharper than ever.

Neurologists are making headway in informing these debates. For starters, researchers using state-of-the-art imaging techniques have found differences in several brain regions of ADHD and non-ADHD children of similar ages. On average, both the frontal lobe and the cerebellum are smaller in ADHD brains, as are the parietal and temporal lobes. ADHD seems to be the result of abnormal information processing in these brain regions, which are responsible for emotion and control over impulses and movements.

Yet these variations do not indicate any basic mental deficiency. Currently physicians see the disorder as an extreme within the natural variability of human behavior. On neuropsychological tests such as letter-sequence recognition on a computer, ADHD children have varied but frequently slower reaction times. The reason, experts now believe, is that neural information processing—the foundation of experience and behavior—may break down, especially when many competing demands suddenly flood the brain. In this circumstance or when faced with tasks requiring speed, thoroughness or endurance, the performance of ADHD brains decreases dramatically compared with the brains of other children. A lack of stimulation, on the other hand, quickly leads to boredom.

The attention deficit is particularly evident whenever children are asked to control their behav-

THINKSTOCK/GETTY IMAGES

ior—stopping an impulsive action or maintaining a high level of performance in a given task. The problem is not so much a lack of attention per se but a rapid drop in the ability to continually pay attention.

A different phenomenon, however, gives hyperactive children the uncontrollable urge to move. Together with the cerebellum, which coordinates movement, various control systems within and underneath the cerebral cortex are responsible for motor functions. This region is where the neurons

pamine release strengthens the neural connections that lead to a desired behavior when a reward stimulus is presented. But when dopamine is absent, rewards that are minor or presented at the wrong time have no effect.

Genes or Environment

One question that arises from all these findings is why specific brain regions are smaller than others and why certain brain functions are weak or

The performance problem is not so much a lack of attention per se but a rapid drop in the ability to continually pay attention.

of the motor cortex, the basal ganglia and the thalamus come together. The motor cortex represents the final stage of neural processing, after which motor impulses are sent to muscles. When activity in these regions is not balanced, children have difficulty preparing for, selecting and executing movements because they cannot adequately control or inhibit their motor system. Complex movements that require precise sequencing are initiated too early and then overshoot their target. Hyperactivity also often goes hand in hand with deficits in fine motor coordination and an inability of children to stop speech from bursting forth uncontrollably.

In general, the underlying trait of impulsivity is linked to the development of the brain's so-called executive function: the ability to plan and to monitor working memory. Executive function develops over time as the brain matures. In children with ADHD, however, it tends to remain rudimentary. Anatomically, the executive function stems from neural networks in the prefrontal cortex—the so-called anterior attentional system. Together with the posterior attentional system, located largely in the parietal lobes, it tracks and regulates behavior.

While trying to navigate life without a strong ability to monitor and plan, ADHD children are often in constant battle with their emotions. They are barely able to control their feelings, and they do not endure frustration well. They easily become excited and impatient and tend toward hostility. They also find it hard to motivate themselves for certain tasks. And they are apt to grasp at the first reward that comes their way, no matter how small, rather than wait for a larger, more attractive payoff.

Dopamine plays an important role in the limbic system, which addresses emotional challenges, and ADHD children typically have low levels of this neurotransmitter. Normally, for example, do-

unbalanced. Genes may play a considerable role. Comprehensive metastudies of parents and children and identical and fraternal twins, such as those conducted by Anita Thapar, then at the University of Manchester in England, in 1999, Philip Asherson of King's College in London in 2001, and Susan Sprich of Massachusetts General Hospital in 2001, show that heredity greatly influences the occurrence of ADHD. For example, children of parents who have had ADHD are far more likely to suffer similar symptoms. The studies indicate that approximately 80 percent of ADHD cases can be traced to genetic factors.

As a result, researchers have been busily trying to identify which genes might be different in ADHD children. High on the suspect list are genes involved in transferring information between neurons. This group includes genes for proteins that influence the circulation of dopamine at the synapses between neurons—for example, proteins that clear away old messenger molecules so new ones can come through. So far researchers have found that receptor mediation of the dopamine signal is too weak in some patients, and dopamine reuptake is too rapid in others.

The genetics work seems to indicate that behavior problems are associated with insufficient regulation of dopamine metabolism, which derails neural information processing. The neurotransmitter norepinephrine may play a role, too. Although the genetic links between norepinephrine and its receptors and transporters are not as clearly understood as those for dopamine, medications such as atomoxetine that inhibit norepinephrine reuptake by neurons do improve symptoms.

When coupled, the neurotransmitter and brain-imaging evidence imply that the brains of ADHD children may be organized and function

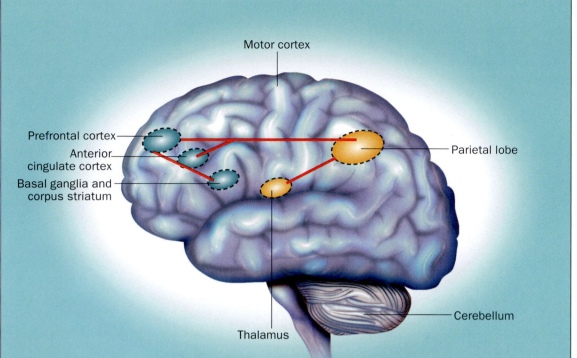

Uncommon activity in various brain regions is associated with hyperactive behavior in ADHD children. Regions are typically part of the anterior attentional system (*green*) which depends on the neurotransmitter dopamine, or the posterior attentional system and norepinephrine (*yellow*).

Labels on figure:
Motor cortex
Prefrontal cortex
Anterior cingulate cortex
Basal ganglia and corpus striatum
Parietal lobe
Cerebellum
Thalamus

differently from an early age. These organic disparities may actually be the cause of behavioral changes and not a consequence of them, as has sometimes been suggested. Another piece of evidence is that in some cases, as children mature, certain physiological peculiarities—such as the size of the corpus striatum—become normal, and ADHD fades.

Still, ADHD cannot yet be tied neatly to known physical, genetic factors. Experts believe that the gene loci discovered to date explain at most 5 percent of problematic behaviors. If more fundamental gene variations are at fault, they have not yet been found. The probability of developing a hyperactivity disorder depends on a combination of many different genes.

Furthermore, there is wide variability in the degree to which these genetic factors are expressed. That means environmental influences must certainly play a role. For example, alcohol and nicotine consumption by a mother during pregnancy tends to increase the risk of ADHD in offspring, in much the same way they contribute to extreme prematurity, low birth weight and food allergies.

On the other hand, it is also true that mothers with a genetic predisposition to ADHD have a propensity to smoke and drink during pregnancy. They tend to make basic child-rearing errors, too, such as failing to establish clear rules and effective limits. A chaotic household can strength-en biological ADHD tendencies, leading to a vicious cycle.

Other psychosocial factors, including a non-supportive school environment, marital crises or psychological problems arising between parents, and poor parent-child attachment can also transform a latent tendency into a full-blown disorder.

Medication Dispute

Recent findings about deficits in brain function and neurotransmitters make it clear why certain drugs are likely treatments. And yet the role of environment suggests that behavioral therapy can also be effective. Today uncertainty surrounds both options, and the increasing use of medication has proved divisive. Opinion runs from euphoric endorsement to outright rejection.

The body of evidence suggests that neurotransmitter systems need to be targeted. Psychostimulants such as amphetamine sulfates and methylphenidate, marketed under such names as Ritalin, have had widespread success. Numerous clinical studies show that these medications can

(The Authors)

ARIBERT ROTHENBERGER and TOBIAS BANASCHEWSKI are both in the clinic for child psychiatry and psychotherapy at the University of Göttingen in Germany. Rothenberger is a professor and director of the clinic. Banaschewski is the clinic's chief physician.

SIGANIM *Gehirn & Geist*

Neurofeedback is the newest treatment alternative that therapists are exploring to combat ADHD. It is based on the finding that the electrical brain activity of ADHD children often differs from that of their peers. In this scheme, children play special computer games to learn how to consciously influence their brain waves—and therefore their behavior. For example, they can make themselves calmer and more attentive by strengthening certain electrical activity and decreasing other activity. Sounds, music or movie clips reward them when they can elicit a desired change.

In one game (*photograph*), a child wearing electrodes watches a cartoon of a pole-vaulting mouse. The mouse can only clear the bar when the pole turns red. This feat occurs when the child concentrates, but the pole turns blue when the child does not.

Children in neurofeedback therapy usually undergo three or four 30- to 40-minute sessions a week for six to 10 weeks. Attention, concentration, impulsivity and mild forms of hyperactivity frequently improve. A child's feelings of self-esteem also improve because he sees that he can control his own behavior. Many succeed in transferring the concentration skills they develop to their schoolwork.   —*A.R. and T.B.*

decrease or eliminate behavioral disorders in 70 to 90 percent of patients.

Administering stimulants to hyperactive children might seem counterintuitive. Yet these substances fix the genetically based dopamine imbalance in the parts of the brain responsible for self-regulation, impulse control and perception. In effect, they prevent the overly rapid reuptake of dopamine at synapses. Other substances with similar modes of action, such as the norepinephrine reuptake inhibitor atomoxetine, work equally well.

Many parents are understandably nervous about subjecting their children to a long-term regimen of medication. News that Ritalin use may be implicated in Parkinson's disease, a dopamine deficiency illness, has added to the worry. Such a connection was suspected because rats that received methylphenidate before sexual maturity exhibited fewer than normal dopamine transporters in their striatum. But to date, not a single case of Parkinson's has been attributed to the use of Ritalin during childhood, and on average Parkinson's patients do not have a history of taking psychostimulants more frequently than other people. Nevertheless, many parents may fear that long-term treatment with psychoactive drugs could leave their child vulnerable to drug or medication abuse in the future.

Recently, however, Timothy E. Wilens and his colleagues at Harvard Medical School laid these concerns to rest with a large-scale metastudy. It turns out that the use of psychostimulants significantly *reduces* the risk of future abuse. In comparing ADHD adults with comparable symptoms, those who had not received ADHD medications as children were three times more likely to succumb to drug addiction later in life than those who had received medication.

Drugs Plus Behavior

This does not mean that physicians should prescribe drugs lightly. And under no circumstances should doctors, parents or patients rely exclusively on medication. Studies show that adding behavioral therapy greatly enhances improvements. It also can teach children how to overcome any kind of problematic behavior that might arise in their lifetime. Children learn how to observe and control themselves. Unless ADHD erupts in its most extreme form, behavioral therapy should be the initial treatment of choice. If a child shows no significant signs of improvement after several months, a drug regimen can then be considered.

ARIBERT ROTHENBERGER

For the youngest children—those of preschool age—psychostimulants should generally be avoided. Parents should instead try to work daily with their children on their behavior. Parents would also do well to draw on the expertise of preschool teachers, who see many different children with a wide range of challenges.

A comprehensive examination conducted in 2000 by the National Institute of Mental Health rated the effectiveness of medical and behavioral treatments of ADHD. Conducted over two years, the Multimodal Treatment Study of Children with

Parents also need aids for dealing with trying situations. They can receive guidance in parent training programs that focus on their child-rearing skills as well as their child's interactions within the family. One common recommendation is to set up written schedules with children so that getting ready for school, for example, does not turn into a contest every morning. Clear rules, specific expectations and known consequences as well as reward points for desired behaviors can all be effective. Particularly with teenagers, parents and even siblings should be included in family therapy.

Studies strongly suggest that a combination of drug and behavioral therapies leads to the highest success.

ADHD included 579 ADHD children at six different university medical centers. The principal investigators divided the test subjects, all of whom were between the ages of seven and nine, into four groups that had different treatment plans. The results strongly suggest that a combination of drug and behavioral therapies leads to the highest success:

- Routine daily treatment with prescribed medication normalized behavior in 25 percent of children treated.
- Intensive behavioral therapy without medication ended with 34 percent of patients exhibiting no further remarkable symptoms.
- Carefully tailored medical treatment with accompanying counseling for the child and parents helped 56 percent of the children.
- A combination of medication and behavioral therapy resulted in a success rate of 68 percent.

Always Count to 10

These findings allow us to draw concrete conclusions about how parents and educators might best help ADHD children. With or without drugs, it is imperative that children be taught how to handle tasks with more organization and less impulsivity. One common tool, for example, is teaching them to count to 10 before carrying out an impulse, such as jumping up from a table at school. Wall posters or cards shaped like stop signs can remind children to use the various devices they have learned in the heat of a moment. Older children and teenagers can learn how to make detailed plans and how to follow through when complicated tasks threaten to shut them down—for example, when they must straighten a messy bedroom.

As neuroscience progresses, therapists continue to try to refine which mixes of drugs and behavioral therapy are best for which types of ADHD. More work is needed. Little is known, for example, about what occurs in the brains of ADHD children between birth and the time they enter school. One conclusion has become increasingly clear, however: the varying combinations of behaviors cannot be grouped into a picture of a single disorder. Researchers are now trying to define subgroups that are more coherent in terms of symptoms and neurological causes. To this end, they are looking at other disturbances that are often associated with attention deficit or hyperactivity; approximately 80 percent of ADHD children suffer from at least one other challenge, such as nervous tics, antisocial behavior, anxiety, or reading and spelling problems.

In the meantime, as parents and teachers do the best they can, they must remember that ADHD children possess many positive traits. They tend to be free-spirited, inquisitive, energetic and funny as well as intelligent and creative. Their behavior is often spontaneous, helpful and sensitive. Many ADHD children are talented multitaskers, last-minute specialists and improvisationalists. Parents and educators should encourage these strengths and let their children know whenever possible that these qualities are highly valued. That will help them feel less under attack, a relief that all by itself can help them begin to turn the corner.

(Further Reading)

◆ **Driven to Distraction: Recognizing and Coping with Attention Deficit Disorder from Childhood through Adulthood.** Reprint edition. Edward M. Hallowell and John J. Ratey. Touchstone, 1995.

Islands
OF GENIUS

Artistic brilliance and a dazzling memory can sometimes accompany autism and other developmental disorders

By Darold A. Treffert and Gregory L. Wallace

PHOTOGRAPHS BY ETHAN HILL

Leslie Lemke is a musical virtuoso. At the age of 14 he played, flawlessly and without hesitation, Tchaikovsky's Piano Concerto No. 1 after hearing it for the first time while listening to a television movie several hours earlier. Lemke had never had a piano lesson—and he still has not had one. He is blind and developmentally disabled, and he has cerebral palsy. Lemke plays and sings thousands of pieces at concerts in the U.S. and abroad, and he improvises and composes as well.

Richard Wawro's artwork is internationally renowned, collected by Margaret Thatcher and Pope John Paul II, among others. A London art professor was "thunderstruck" by the oil crayon drawings that Wawro did as a child, describing them as an "incredible phenomenon rendered with the precision of a mechanic and the vision of a poet." Wawro, who lives in Scotland, is autistic.

Kim Peek is a walking encyclopedia. He has memorized more than 7,600 books. He can recite the highways that go to each American city, town or county, along with the area and zip codes, television stations and telephone networks that serve them. If you tell him your date of birth, he can tell you what day of the week it fell on and what day

Kim Peek, who is developmentally disabled, knows more than 7,600 books by heart as well as every area code, highway, zip code and television station in the U.S. He provided the inspiration for the character Raymond Babbitt in the 1988 movie *Rain Man.*

Kim Peek

Of the known savants, at least half are autistic and the remainder have some other kind of developmental disorder.

Much remains mysterious about savant syndrome. Nevertheless, advances in brain imaging are permitting a more complete view of the condition, and a long-standing theory of left hemispheric damage has found support in these imaging studies. In addition, new reports of the sudden appearance of savant syndrome in people with certain forms of dementia have raised the intriguing possibility that some aspects of such genius lie dormant in all of us.

Down's Definition

Descriptions of savant syndrome appear in the scientific literature as early as 1789. Benjamin Rush, the "father of American psychiatry," described the lightning-quick calculating ability of Thomas Fuller, who understood little math more complex than counting. When Fuller was asked how many seconds a man had lived by the time he was 70 years, 17 days and 12 hours old, he gave the correct answer of 2,210,500,800 a minute and a half later—and he had taken into account 17 leap years.

It was not until 1887, however, that the remarkable coexistence of deficiency and superiori-

> # Encouraging the exceptional abilities of savants can help them develop greater social skills, language acquisition and independence.

of the week it will be when you turn 65 "and can retire." Peek can identify most classical compositions and knows the date the music was published or first performed as well as the composer's birthplace and dates of birth and death. He is also developmentally disabled and depends on his father for many of his basic daily needs. His abilities provided the inspiration for the character Raymond Babbitt, whom Dustin Hoffman played in the 1988 movie *Rain Man*.

Lemke, Wawro and Peek all have savant syndrome, an uncommon but spectacular condition in which people with various developmental disabilities, including autism, possess astonishing islands of ability and brilliance that stand in jarring juxtaposition to their overall mental handicap. Savant syndrome is seen in about one in 10 people with autism and in approximately one in 2,000 people with brain damage or mental retardation.

ty was more completely laid out. That year J. Langdon Down, who is best known for having identified Down syndrome, described 10 people with savant syndrome. He had met these fascinating individuals during his 30 years as superintendent of the Earlswood Asylum in London. He coined the now discarded term "idiot savant," using the then accepted classification of an idiot as someone with an IQ of less than 25, combined with a derivative of the French word *savoir*, which means "to know."

More than a century has passed since Down's description. Today we know much more about this perplexing set of abilities from the 100 or so cases described in the scientific literature. Savant syndrome generally occurs in people with IQs between 40 and 70—although it can occur in some with IQs up to 114 or even higher. It disproportionately affects males, with four to six male sa-

Leslie Lemke is blind and has never studied piano. Although he suffers from cerebral palsy and is developmentally disabled, he composes music and is able to play thousands of pieces flawlessly, even when he has heard them only once.

vants for every one female. And it can be congenital or acquired later in life following disease (such as encephalitis) or brain injury.

Narrow Repertoire

The skills that savant syndrome gives rise to are limited for the most part, and they tend to be based in the right hemisphere. That is, they are predominantly nonsymbolic, artistic, visual and motor. They include music, art, mathematics, forms of calculating, and an assortment of other abilities, such as mechanical aptitude or spatial skills. In contrast, left hemisphere skills are more sequential, logical and symbolic; they include language and speech specialization [see "The Split Brain Revisited," by Michael S. Gazzaniga; SCIENTIFIC AMERICAN, July 1998].

Most musical savants have perfect pitch and

Richard Wawro is an internationally renowned Scottish painter who has been exhibiting his work since he was 17 years old. He is autistic.

perform with amazing ease, most often on the piano. Some are able to create complex compositions. And for some reason, musical genius often seems to accompany blindness and mental retardation, as it does for Lemke. One of the most famous savants was "Blind Tom" Bethune, who lived from 1849 to 1908. In his time, he was referred to as "the eighth wonder of the world." Although he could speak fewer than 100 words, he could play beautifully more than 7,000 pieces on the piano, including many of his own works. (Some of his compositions were recorded by musician John Davis and released in 2000.)

For their part, savant visual artists use a variety of media, although they most frequently express themselves through drawing and sculpture. Artis-

(Emerging Savants)

Researchers have discovered that certain patients who develop frontotemporal dementia (FTD) can paint beautifully when they previously had no such talent. In short, they have become savantlike as dementia has taken hold. This painting of horses was made by one such patient, a 64-year-old woman. Bruce L. Miller of the University of California at San Francisco has examined many FTD patients and has documented damage to the left side of their brain.

One theory suggests that savant skills may emerge in the more artistic right hemisphere as a way of compensating for damage in the left. In this SPECT image (*left*) of an FTD patient, enhanced blood flow can be seen in a part of the right hemisphere (*red*). —*D.A.T. and G.L.W.*

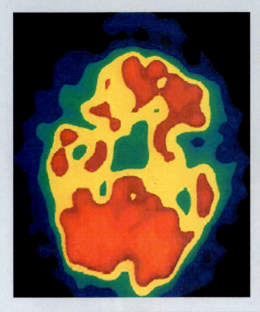

tic savant Alonzo Clemons, for example, can see a fleeting image of an animal on a television screen and in less than 20 minutes sculpt a perfect replica of that animal. His wax model will be correct in every detail, every fiber and muscle and proportion.

Mathematical savants calculate incredibly rapidly and often have a particular facility with prime numbers. Curiously, the obscure skill of calendar calculating that Peek demonstrates is not confined to mathematical savants; it seems to coexist with many different skills.

Several other abilities appear less frequently. A rare savant may have extensive language ability—that is, the capacity to memorize many languages but not to understand them. Other unusual traits include heightened olfactory, tactile and visual sensitivity; outstanding knowledge in fields such as history, neurophysiology, statistics or navigation; and spatial ability. For instance, a musical and blind savant named Ellen can navigate in thick forests or other unfamiliar spaces without running into objects. Ellen also has a perfect appreciation of passing time despite the fact that she doesn't have access to a watch or clock, even in Braille.

This ability was discovered one day when her mother let her listen to the "time lady" on the telephone. After listening for a short while to the recorded voice intone the hour and seconds, Ellen apparently set her own internal clock. Since then, she has been able to tell what time it is to the second, no matter the season.

Savant skills are always linked to a remarkable memory. This memory is deep, focused and based on habitual recitation. But it entails little understanding of what is being described. Some early observers aptly called this "memory without reckoning." Down himself used the phrase "verbal adhesion" to characterize it. One of his patients was a boy who had read the six-volume *History of the*

(The Authors)

DAROLD A. TREFFERT and GREGORY L. WALLACE share a long-standing interest in savant syndrome. Treffert (dtreffert@pol.net) is a clinical professor of psychiatry at the University of Wisconsin–Madison and has done research on autism and savant syndrome since 1962, the year he met his first savant. Wallace (gregwallace@mail.nih.gov) is a research fellow in the Child Psychiatry Branch of the National Institute of Mental Health. He is conducting studies on why individuals with autism are more likely to develop savant skills.

Alonzo Clemons can create perfect wax replicas of any animal he sees, no matter how briefly. His bronze statues are sold by a gallery in Aspen, Colo., and have earned him national repute. Clemons is developmentally disabled.

Decline and Fall of the Roman Empire, by Edward Gibbon, and could recite it back word for word, although he did so without any comprehension.

Although they share many talents, including memory, savants vary enormously in their levels of ability. So-called splinter-skill savants have a preoccupation and mild expertise with, say, the memorization of sports trivia and license plate numbers. Talented savants have musical or artistic gifts that are conspicuously above what would be expected of someone with their handicaps. And prodigious savants are those very uncommon people whose abilities are so advanced that they would be distinctive even if they were to occur in a normal person. Probably fewer than 50 prodigious savants are alive at the moment.

Whatever their talents, savants usually main-

nine-year-old boy who had become mute, deaf and paralyzed on the right side when a bullet damaged his left hemisphere. After the accident, unusual savant mechanical skills emerged. He was able to repair multigeared bicycles and to design contraptions, such as a punching bag that would weave and bob like a real opponent.

The findings of Bernard Rimland of the Autism Research Institute in San Diego support this idea as well. Rimland maintains the largest database in the world on people with autism; he has information on more than 34,000 individuals. He has observed that the savant skills most often present in autistic people are those associated with right hemisphere functions and the most deficient abilities are associated with left hemisphere functions.

In the late 1980s Norman Geschwind and Al-

No one knows how savants can do what they do, but research suggests injury to the left brain causes the right brain to compensate.

tain them over the course of their life. With continued use, the abilities are sustained and sometimes even improve. And in almost all cases, there is no dreaded trade-off of these wonderful abilities with the acquisition of language, socialization or daily living skills. Instead the talents often help savants to establish some kind of normal routine or way of life [see box on next page].

Looking to the Left Hemisphere

Although specialists today are better able to characterize the talents of savants, no overarching theory can describe exactly how or why savants do what they do. The most powerful explanation suggests that some injury to the left brain causes the right brain to compensate for the loss. The evidence for this idea has been building for several decades. A 1975 pneumoencephalogram study found left hemispheric damage in 15 of 17 autistic patients; four of them had savant skills. (A pneumoencephalogram was an early and painful imaging technique during which a physician would inject air into a patient's spinal fluid and then x-ray the brain to determine where the air traveled. It is no longer used.)

A dramatic study published by T. L. Brink in 1980 lent further credence to the possibility that changes to the left hemisphere were important to savant syndrome. Brink, a psychologist at Crafton Hills College in California, described a normal

bert M. Galaburda of Harvard University offered an explanation for some causes of left hemispheric damage—and for the higher number of male savants. In their book *Cerebral Lateralization,* the two neurologists point out that the left hemisphere of the brain normally completes its development later than the right and is therefore subject to prenatal influences—some of them detrimental—for a longer period. In the male fetus, circulating testosterone can act as one of these detrimental influences by slowing growth and impairing neuronal function in the more vulnerable left hemisphere. As a result, the right brain often compensates, becoming larger and more dominant in males. The greater male-to-female ratio is seen not just in savant syndrome but in other forms of central nervous system dysfunction, such as dyslexia, delayed speech, stuttering, hyperactivity and autism.

Newly Savant

In recent years, more data have emerged to support the left hemisphere hypothesis. In 1998 Bruce L. Miller of the University of California at San Francisco examined five elderly patients with frontotemporal dementia (FTD), one form of presenile dementia. These patients had developed artistic skills with the onset and progression of their dementia. They were able to make meticulous copies of artworks and to paint beautifully. Consistent with that in savants, the creativity in

(Living with Savant Syndrome)

A few reports in the literature suggest that when savants are encouraged to acquire better language skills they lose their special artistic talents. Perhaps the most famous of these cases is that of Nadia, a girl with autism who by the age of three was producing astounding drawings. When she turned seven, Nadia entered a school for autistic children that focused on verbal abilities; by the time she was a teenager, Nadia was more verbal but could no longer create brilliant and intricate drawings.

This trade-off between talent and language or socialization is not something we have witnessed. Instead the exceptional abilities of savants have proved to be strengths that are built on and used as a conduit toward normalization; these skills have helped individuals develop improved social skills, better language acquisition and greater independence. Savants gain a sense of accomplishment because of their talent; that sense, in turn, allows them to participate more fully in the world. Musical prodigy Leslie Lemke has become more animated, performing concerts and interacting with audiences. Painter Richard Wawro feels delight and excitement when he finishes a work, and he seeks out celebration. And memory wizard Kim Peek has emerged from the social isolation that characterized him before the movie *Rain Man* was made; he now travels the country talking to hundreds of school groups.

Fortunately, simultaneously encouraging savant abilities and normalization is now the generally accepted approach to such individuals' care. Savants are being placed in some classes for the gifted and talented, an opportunity that promotes social growth for both them and their

Ferry boat to Tiree, Scotland, was painted in 1978 by Richard Wawro. Wawro is cared for by his father, who enthusiastically supports his painting. Most researchers believe that encouraging such skills may help savants develop better social skills.

classmates. Some new programs, such as the one at Hope University in Anaheim, Calif., cater entirely to these exceptional individuals. Others include people with similar disorders as well; for example, music and art camps have been established for those with Williams syndrome, many of whom have savantlike musical skills [see "Williams Syndrome and the Brain," by Howard M. Lenhoff, Paul P. Wang, Frank Greenberg and Ursula Bellugi; SCIENTIFIC AMERICAN, December 1997]. Nurturing the talent of these people is the most fulfilling approach.
—*D.A.T. and G.L.W.*

these five individuals was visual, not verbal. Single-photon-emission computed tomography (SPECT) showed that injury was predominantly on the left side of the brain. Miller examined seven other patients who had developed musical or artistic ability after the appearance of FTD. He found damage on the left as well.

Miller, Craig Hou, then at Washington University, and others then compared these images with those of a nine-year-old artistic autistic savant named DB. SPECT scans of DB revealed a higher-than-normal blood flow in part of his neocortex but decreased flow in his left temporal lobe. (The neocortex is involved with high-level cognitive function; the temporal lobe is responsible for some aspects of memory and emotion.) Miller is hoping to study other artistic savants to see if the findings hold true for them as well. But the fact that DB and older FTD patients with newfound

savant skills have the same pathology is quite striking and suggests that researchers will soon be able to identify precisely the neurological features associated with savant syndrome.

The seemingly limitless memory of savants will most likely be harder to pinpoint physiologically. Mortimer Mishkin of the National Institute of Mental Health has proposed different neural circuits for memory, including a higher-level corticolimbic circuit for what is generally referred to as explicit, semantic or cognitive memory, and a lower-level corticostriatal circuit for the more primitive habit memory referred to as implicit or procedural memory. The memory of savants seems to be the noncognitive habit form.

The same factors that produce left hemispheric damage may be instrumental in producing damage to higher-level memory circuits. As a result, savants may be forced to rely on more primitive, but spared, habit memory circuits. Perhaps brain injuries—whether they result from hormones, disease, or prenatal or subsequent injury—produce in some instances certain right-brain skills linked with habit memory function. In those situations, savant syndrome may appear.

Rain Man in Us All?

The emergence of savantlike skills in people with dementia raises profound questions about the buried potential in all of us. Accordingly, several researchers are seeking to unlock what has been called the "little Rain Man in each of us." One

some procedures—including hypnosis; interviews of subjects under the influence of the barbiturate sodium amytal, which induces relaxation; and brain stimulation during neurosurgery—provide evidence that a huge reservoir of memories lies dormant in every individual. Dreams can also revive those memories or trigger new abilities.

No model of brain function will be complete until it can explain this rare condition. Now that we have the tools to examine brain structure and function, such studies can be correlated with detailed neuropsychological testing of savants. We hope the anecdotal case reports that have charac-

Experts believe each of us can tap into our own islands of savant intelligence that are simply overwhelmed by everyday cognition.

group has used a technique called repetitive transcranial magnetic stimulation (rTMS) in 17 normal individuals, eight male and nine female. Tracy Morrell of the University of South Australia, Robyn L. Young of Flinders University in Adelaide and Michael C. Ridding of Adelaide University applied magnetic stimulation to the area in the left temporal lobe that Miller identified as damaged in his FTD patients.

In its study, the team reports that only two of the participants experienced a series of short-lived skills, such as calendar calculating, artistic ability and enhanced habit memory. Other subjects discovered a new skill here and there, also lasting just a few hours. The researchers suggest that savant skills may be limited to a small percentage of the normal population, much as they are limited to a small percentage of the disabled population.

Nevertheless, many experts believe that real potential exists to tap into islands of savant intelligence. Allan Snyder and John Mitchell of the Australian National University in Canberra argue that savant brain processes occur in each of us but are overwhelmed by more sophisticated conceptual cognition. Autistic savants, they conclude, "have privileged access to lower levels of information not normally available through introspection."

Our view is also that all of us have some of the same circuitry and pathways intrinsic to savant functioning but that these are less accessible—in part because we tend to be a left-brain society. Sometimes, though, we can find elements of the savant in ourselves. At certain moments, we just "get" something or discover a new ability. And

terized the literature on this topic for the past century will soon be replaced by data comparing and contrasting groups of normal and disabled people, including prodigies, geniuses and savants.

A Window into the Brain

Savant syndrome provides a unique window into the brain with regard to questions of general intelligence versus multiple forms of intelligence. It may also shed light on brain plasticity and central nervous system compensation, recruitment and repair—areas of research that are vital in understanding and treating such diverse conditions as stroke, paralysis and Alzheimer's disease.

But savant syndrome has relevance outside the scientific realm. Many lessons can be learned from these remarkable people and their equally remarkable families, caretakers, therapists and teachers. One of the greatest lessons is that they have been shaped by far more than neural circuitry. The savants thrive because of the reinforcement provided by the unconditional love, belief and determination of those who care for them. Savant syndrome promises to take us further than we have ever been toward understanding both the brain and human potential.

(Further Reading)

◆ **Emergence of Artistic Talent in Frontotemporal Dementia.**
 B. Miller, J. Cummings and F. Mishkin et al. in *Neurology*, Vol. 51, No. 4, pages 978–982; October 1, 1998.
◆ **Extraordinary People: Understanding Savant Syndrome.**
 Darold A. Treffert. iUniverse.com, Inc., 2000.
◆ **www.savantsyndrome.com**

New Movement in PARKINSON'S

Recent genetic and cellular discoveries are among the advances pointing to improved treatments for this increasingly common disorder

By Andres M. Lozano and Suneil K. Kalia

Parkinson's disease, first described in the early 1800s

by British physician James Parkinson as "shaking palsy," is among the most prevalent neurological disorders. According to the United Nations, at least four million people worldwide have it; in North America, estimates run from 500,000 to one million, with about 50,000 diagnosed every year. These figures are expected to double by 2040 as the world's elderly population grows; indeed, Parkinson's and other neurodegenerative illnesses common in the elderly (such as Alzheimer's and amyotrophic lateral sclerosis) are on their way to overtaking cancer as a leading cause of death. But the disease is not entirely one of the aged: 50 percent of patients acquire it after age 60; the other half are affected before then. Furthermore, better diagnosis has made experts increasingly aware that the disorder can attack those younger than 40.

So far researchers and clinicians have found no way to slow, stop or prevent Parkinson's. Although treatments do exist—including drugs and deep-brain stimulation—these therapies alleviate symptoms, not causes. In recent years, however, several promising developments have occurred. In particular, investigators who study the role proteins play have linked miscreant proteins to genetic underpinnings of the disease. Such findings are feeding optimism that fresh angles of attack can be identified.

As its 19th-century name suggests—and as many people know from the educational efforts of prominent Parkinson's sufferers such as Janet Reno, Muhammad Ali and Michael J. Fox—the disease is characterized by movement disorders. Tremor in the hands, arms and elsewhere, limb rigidity, slowness of movement, and impaired balance and coordination are among the disease's hallmarks. In addition, some patients have trouble walking, talking, sleeping, urinating and performing sexually.

These impairments result from neurons dying. Although the victim cells are many and found throughout the brain, those producing the neurotransmitter dopamine in a region called the substantia nigra are particularly hard-hit. These dopaminergic nerve cells are key components of the basal ganglia, a complex circuit deep within the brain that fine-tunes and coordinates movement [see box on page 20]. Initially the brain can function normally as it loses dopaminergic neurons in the substantia nigra, even though it cannot replace the dead cells. But when half or more of these specialized cells disappear, the brain can no longer cover for them. The deficit then produces the same effect that losing air traffic control does at a major airport. Delays, false starts, cancellations and, ultimately, chaos pervade as parts of the brain involved in motor control—the thalamus, basal ganglia and cerebral cortex—no longer function as an integrated and orchestrated unit.

Proteins Behaving Badly

IN MANY PARKINSON'S CASES, the damage can be seen in autopsies as clumps of proteins within the substantia nigra's dopaminergic neurons. Such protein masses also feature in Alzheimer's and Huntington's—but in

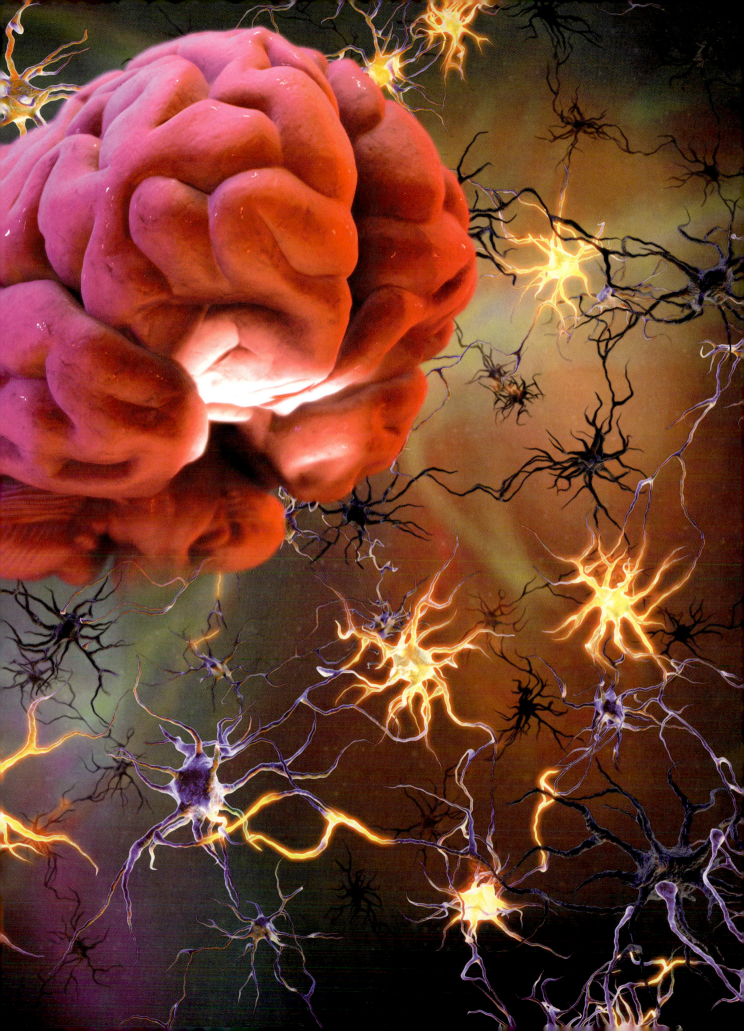

Parkinson's they are called Lewy bodies, after the German pathologist who first observed them in 1912. Like researchers studying those other neurodegenerative diseases, Parkinson's investigators heatedly debate whether the protein clusters themselves cause destruction or are protective and endeavoring to remove toxic molecules from the neurons. Regardless of their position, however, most agree that understanding these accumulations is key to understanding Parkinson's.

Two cellular processes occupy a central place in this emerging story: protein folding and protein elimination. Cells synthesize proteins, which are chains of amino acids, based on instructions written in the DNA of genes. As the proteins are produced, molecules called chaperones fold them into the three-dimensional form they are supposed to take. These chaperones also refold proteins that have become unfolded.

If the chaperone system fails for some reason, proteins not properly folded in the first place or those that did not correctly refold become targeted for disposal by what is called the ubiquitin-proteasome system. First, ubiquitin, a small protein, is attached to a misshapen protein in a process called ubiquitinylation. Such tagging is repeated until ubiquitin chains of varying lengths end up draped over the ill-fated protein. These chains become the kiss of death. They alert the nerve cell's proteasome, a garbage disposal system, to the existence of the bedecked protein. The proteasome then digests it into its constituent amino acids. Aaron Ciechanover and Avram Hershko of Technion-Israel Institute of Technology and Irwin Rose of the University of California at Irvine were awarded the

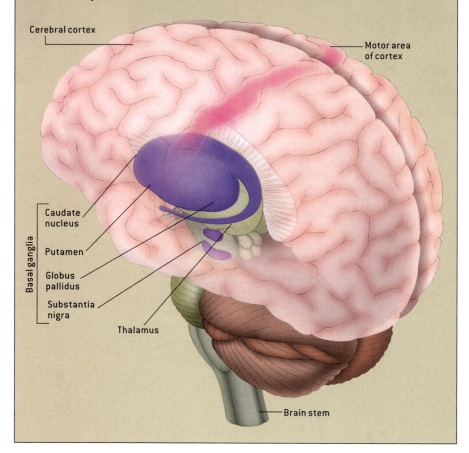

BRAIN REGIONS AFFECTED BY PARKINSON'S

Most cell death occurs in the substantia nigra, which controls voluntary movement and helps to regulate mood. Although the rest of the brain can initially compensate, it can no longer do so when 50 to 80 percent of the cells in the substantia nigra have been lost. At that point, other parts of the brain engaged in motor control, including the rest of the basal ganglia (of which the substantia nigra is part), the thalamus and the cerebral cortex, can no longer work together, and movement becomes disjointed and uncontrollable.

Cerebral cortex

Motor area of cortex

Basal ganglia
Caudate nucleus
Putamen
Globus pallidus
Substantia nigra

Thalamus

Brain stem

2004 Nobel Prize in Chemistry for their work describing this system.

In the past few years, many scientists have come to believe that Parkinson's emerges when the chaperone and ubiquitin-proteasome systems malfunction.

They reason that the disease process might go something like this: some form of injury to neurons of the substantia nigra triggers a cascade of cellular stresses [see "Understanding Parkinson's Disease," by Moussa B. H. Youdim and Peter Riederer; SCIENTIFIC AMERICAN, January 1997]. These stresses result in a wealth of misfolded proteins that congregate. This buildup might initially be protective because all the renegade proteins are herded together and thus prevented from causing trouble elsewhere in a cell. Chaperones then set to work refolding, and the disposal system starts eliminating those proteins that cannot be reformed. When the production of poorly folded proteins overwhelms the cell's

Overview/*Proteins and Parkinson's*

- One of the most pervasive neurological diseases, Parkinson's disease cannot be slowed, stopped or prevented. The two standard forms of treatment, medications and surgery, can only reduce symptoms.
- Recent discoveries about how proteins malfunction and the genetic underpinnings of Parkinson's have opened new avenues for research, and investigators are feeling some optimism about finding new treatments.
- Protein folding and disposal systems gone awry now appear to be central to the disorder, and the genetic causes for those failures have come to light.

ability to process them, however, trouble arises: The ubiquitin-proteasome system becomes inhibited, chaperones get depleted, and toxic proteins accumulate. Neuronal cell death follows.

Researchers espousing this hypothesis think it could explain Parkinson's two forms. An estimated 95 percent of patients suffer from sporadic disease—the results of a complex interplay between genes and the environment. When someone with a susceptible genetic background encounters certain environmental factors, such as pesticides or other chemicals [*see box on this page*], the cells in that individual's substantia nigra suffer more stress and accumulate more misfolded proteins than do the same cells in other people. In the remaining 5 percent of patients, Parkinson's appears to be controlled almost entirely by genetics. Discoveries in the past eight years have revealed a connection between mutations and either the buildup of misshapen proteins or the failure of the cell's protective machinery. These genetic insights have been the most exciting developments in the field in years.

The Genetic Frontier

AT THE NATIONAL Institutes of Health in 1997, Mihael H. Polymeropoulos and his colleagues identified a mutation in a gene for a protein called alpha-synuclein in Italian and Greek families with an inherited form of Parkinson's. It is an autosomal dominant mutation, meaning just one copy (from the mother or the father) can trigger the disease. Mutations in the *alpha-synuclein* gene are extremely rare and insignificant in the worldwide burden of Parkinson's (they account for far less than 1 percent of patients), but identification of the link between the encoded protein and Parkinson's set off an explosion of activity—in part because alpha-synuclein, normal or otherwise, was soon found to be one of the proteins that accumulates in the protein clumps. Investigators reasoned that a better understanding of how the mutation leads to Parkinson's could suggest clues to the mechanism underlying Lewy body formation in dopamine-producing cells of the substantia

nigra in patients with sporadic disease.

The *alpha-synuclein* gene codes for a very small protein, only 144 amino acids long, which is thought to play a role in signaling between neurons. Mutations result in tiny changes in the amino acid sequence of the protein—in fact, several such mutations are now known, and two of them result in the change of a single amino acid in the sequence. Studies of fruit flies, nematodes (roundworms) and mice have shown that if mutated alpha-synuclein is produced in high amounts, it causes the degeneration of dopaminergic neurons and motor deficits. Other studies have revealed that mutated alpha-synuclein does not fold correctly and accumulates within Lewy bodies. Altered alpha-synuclein also inhibits the ubiquitin-proteasome system and resists

proteasome degradation. In addition, it has recently become clear that having extra copies of the normal *alpha-synuclein* gene can cause Parkinson's.

In 1998, one year after the discovery of the *alpha-synuclein* mutation, Yoshikuni Mizuno of Juntendo University and Nobuyoshi Shimizu of Keio University, both in Japan, identified a second gene, *parkin*, that is mutated in another familial form of Parkinson's. This mutation appears most often in individuals diagnosed before age 40; the younger the age of onset, the more likely the disease is caused by a *parkin* mutation. Although people who inherit a defective copy from both parents (that is, when the mutation is autosomal recessive) inevitably develop the disease, those who carry a single copy of the mutated gene are also at

ENVIRONMENTAL CULPRITS

The idea that Parkinson's disease may be caused by something in the environment has been around for decades. But proof came only in the early 1980s, when J. William Langston of the Parkinson's Institute in Sunnyvale, Calif., studied a group of drug abusers in the San Francisco Bay Area. These young addicts had developed parkinsonian symptoms within days of taking China white, a synthetic heroin. It turned out that the batch contained an impurity called MPTP, a compound that can kill neurons in the brain's substantia nigra region. Through treatment, some of the "frozen addicts," as they came to be called, recovered some movement control; in most, however, the effects were irreversible.

In subsequent years, investigators searched for other compounds with similar effects, and in 2003 their work was bolstered when the National Institute for Environmental Health Sciences put $20 million behind efforts to identify and study environmental causes of Parkinson's. To date, epidemiological and animal studies have linked some cases to high exposure to various pesticides, herbicides and fungicides, including paraquat and maneb. J. Timothy Greenamyre of Emory University has also discovered in animal studies that exposure to rotenone,

SOME PESTICIDES, including one routinely used in organic farming, can induce parkinsonian conditions in animals.

a pesticide often used in organic farming because it is made from natural products, is capable of inducing protein aggregation, killing dopamine-producing neurons, inhibiting the cells' energy-producing organelles and giving rise to motor deficits.

Just as some agents may trigger Parkinson's, others might confer protection. Experts now accept that smoking and coffee drinking can be somewhat protective—although clearly the risks of smoking far outweigh this particular benefit.

—*A.M.L. and S.K.K.*

CURRENT THERAPIES

Physicians take two basic approaches to treating Parkinson's disease. Both can produce striking benefits, but they also have disadvantages, which is why patients and researchers are so eager for new strategies.

MEDICATIONS

The principal treatments encompass medications that mimic dopamine, compounds used to create dopamine in the brain (such as levodopa), and drugs that inhibit the breakdown of dopamine. Several others act on some of the nondopamine systems affected in Parkinson's, including those mediated by the neurotransmitters acetylcholine and glutamate. Many of these drugs help during the initial phases of the disease, but their ongoing use can become problematic. Chief among the long-term adverse effects are unpredictable oscillations between periods of good motor function and periods of freezing, tremor and rigidity. In addition, some of the medications can cause involuntary twisting, writhing movements called dyskinesias, which are particularly prominent in young patients and are extremely disabling.

DEEP-BRAIN STIMULATION

At the turn of the century, investigators discovered that destroying a small number of cells in the brain's motor pathways could reduce parkinsonian tremors. Although the procedure often caused muscle weakness, patients preferred that to the shaking. Then, in 1938, surgeons injured the basal ganglia and found even more marked improvement in Parkinson's patients. It appeared that eliminating the cells that were misbehaving—that is, those misfiring or firing too much—apparently allowed the rest of the brain to function normally. Unfortunately, creating lesions was not a perfect solution. If they were not precisely placed or if they involved both sides of the brain, they could cause severe damage, impairing speech and leading to cognitive problems.

Electrode

Basal ganglia

Implanted wire

Implanted pacemaker

In the 1970s investigators discovered that high-frequency electrical stimulation of parts of the brain could mimic lesions, without reproducing the side effects. Various forms of deep-brain stimulation are used for many neurological disorders today [see "Stimulating the Brain," by Mark S. George; Scientific American, September 2003]. In Parkinson's patients, an electrode is placed in one of two basal ganglia targets—the globus pallidus or subthalamic nucleus—and attached to a pulse-generating device implanted in the chest (below). The pacemaker typically delivers 90-microsecond, three-volt pulses of electricity up to 185 times per second and needs to be replaced every five years.

The pioneers of the technique, Alim Louis Benabid and Pierre Pollak of the University of Grenoble in France, report that such stimulation dramatically reduces tremor and rigidity. Indeed, in the past decade or so it has become a mainstay of treatment, and an estimated 30,000 patients have undergone the surgery. Some have been able to reduce the doses of medicines they take, whereas others have stopped taking them altogether. At the same time, however, deep-brain stimulation cannot prevent the disease from progressing, and it cannot alleviate the problems with cognition, speech and balance that may arise.

Despite the success of deep-brain stimulation, many questions remain. For one thing, it is not clear whether the globus pallidus or the subthalamic nucleus is a better target. In addition, the precise electrical and chemical mechanisms by which electrical energy improves Parkinson's disease remain to be determined, and much of the data are conflicting. For example, researchers used to think deep-brain stimulation worked the same way lesioning did, by inactivating cells. Recently, however, they have learned that the procedure seems to cause faster firing of impulses.   —A.M.L. and S.K.K.

---

greater risk. *Parkin* mutations appear to be more common than *alpha-synuclein* gene mutations, but no good figure on incidence is currently available.

The parkin protein contains a number of amino acid sequences, or domains, common to many proteins. Of particular interest are two so-called RING domains; proteins with these RING domains are involved in the protein degradation pathway. Findings now suggest that neuronal death in this form of Parkinson's stems in part from the failure of the ubiquitinylation component of the

protein disposal system: parkin attaches ubiquitin to misfolded proteins—without it, there is no tagging and no disposal. Our own work has recently shown that a protein called BAG5, which is found in Lewy bodies, can bind to parkin to inhibit its function and cause the death of dopamine-producing neurons.

Interestingly, some patients with *parkin* mutations lack Lewy bodies in their nigral neurons. This observation suggests that proteins may not form aggregates unless the ubiquitinylation process is functioning. It also suggests that when

harmful proteins are not huddled together within Lewy bodies they create cellular havoc. Because patients with *parkin* mutations develop the disease early in life, it seems likely that they miss some initial protection conferred by having toxic proteins quarantined in clumps.

Several other recent discoveries highlight further genetically induced muck-ups in the cellular machinery. In 2002 Vincenzo Bonifati and his colleagues at Erasmus Medical Center in Rotterdam identified a mutation in a gene called *DJ-1*. Like that in *parkin*, this mutation is responsible for an autosomal recessive form of Parkinson's and has been found in Dutch and Italian families. Investigators have seen mutations in another gene, *UCHL1*, in patients with familial Parkinson's. A paper in *Science* just described a mutation in *PINK1* that may lead to metabolic failure and cell death in the substantia nigra. And other work has identified a gene called *LRRK2*, which encodes the protein dardarin (meaning "tremor" in the Basque region, where the affected patients came from). It, too, is involved with metabolism and appears in familial Parkinson's. But researchers are not far along in understanding exactly what all these mutations set wrong.

New Avenues for Treatment

BECAUSE THE INSIGHTS just described involve molecules whose activity could potentially be altered or mimicked by drugs in ways that would limit cell

determine whether such interventions could be made to work in humans.

In addition to pursuing the preliminary leads that have arisen out of the new protein-related and genetic findings, investigators have begun introducing neurotrophic factors—compounds promoting neuronal growth and differentiation—into the brain. These agents not only alleviate symptoms but also promise to protect neurons from damage or even to restore those already harmed.

One line of research in animals, for instance, suggests that a family of proteins called glial cell line-derived neurotrophic factor (GDNF) can enhance the survival of injured dopamine neurons and dramatically reduce parkinsonian symptoms. Steve Gill and his colleagues at Frenchay Hospital in Bristol, England, have embarked on a pilot study to give Parkinson's patients GDNF. Surgeons insert a catheter into the left and right striatum, the main recipients in the basal gan-

us who work in this area feel that this approach is still worth pursuing. It is not unusual in medicine for the first forays into a treatment to be negative. Levodopa, for instance, initially showed no benefit and only unwanted side effects; now it is one of the principal treatments for Parkinson's.

Other researchers are using gene therapy instead of surgery to administer GDNF, hoping the delivered gene will provide a long-term supply of this neurotrophic agent. Jeffrey H. Kordower of Rush Presbyterian-St. Luke's Medical Center in Chicago and Patrick Aebischer of the Neurosciences Institute at the Swiss Federal Institute of Technology and their colleagues engineered a lentivirus to carry the gene for GDNF and deliver it to dopamine-producing striatal cells in four parkinsonian monkeys. The results were impressive: the monkeys' motor problems significantly diminished, and they were unaffected by a

Perhaps one day CHAPERONE-TYPE DRUGS can be developed to limit degeneration in people.

death, the discoveries could lead to therapies that would do more than ease symptoms—they would actually limit the neuronal degeneration responsible for disease progression.

This strategy has yielded two intriguing results. Increasing the levels of chaperones in cells of the substantia nigra has been found to protect against the neurodegeneration set in motion by mutated alpha-synuclein in animals. Recent studies using fruit-fly models of Parkinson's have shown that drugs that induce chaperone activity can offer protection against neurotoxicity. Perhaps one day chaperone-type drugs can be developed to limit degeneration in people, or gene therapy could be devised to trigger the production of needed chaperones. In addition, investigators have found that increasing the amount of normal parkin protein in cells protects against the neurodegeneration resulting from noxious, misfolded proteins. Much more study will be needed, however, to

glia of the dopamine secreted by neurons of the substantia nigra. Minute volumes of GDNF are then continuously infused to the brain from a pump set into the abdomen. The pump holds enough GDNF to last one month and is replenished during an office visit; a syringe pierces the skin and refills the pump reservoir.

Initial results in a handful of patients suggested that symptoms had improved, and PET scans indicated some restoration in dopamine uptake in the striatum and substantia nigra. But the results of a larger, more recent trial have been unconvincing: patients who received saline solution fared no better than those who received GDNF. Nevertheless, many of

subsequent injection of MPTP, a chemical toxic to dopamine neurons of the substantia nigra. The introduced gene induced cells to make the protein for up to six months, after which the experiments were stopped. Based on these studies, scientists at Ceregene in San Diego are using a similar technique to deliver the protein neurturin, a member of the GDNF family. Although the studies are in the preclinical phase, researchers plan to test a gene similar to the gene for neurturin in human patients.

Still other forms of therapy are being investigated. Working with Avigen near San Francisco, Krys Bankiewicz has shown in animals that placing the

THE AUTHORS

ANDRES M. LOZANO and *SUNEIL K. KALIA* have worked together for several years, studying various aspects of Parkinson's disease. Lozano, who was born in Spain and obtained his M.D. from the University of Ottawa, is professor and R. R. Tasker Chair in Stereotactic and Functional Neurosurgery at the Toronto Western Hospital and the University of Toronto. He has devoted his career to understanding the causes of Parkinson's and developing novel surgical treatments. Kalia recently completed his doctoral degree working with Lozano. His research focused on the role of chaperone molecules in Parkinson's.

gene for an enzyme called aromatic amino acid decarboxylase in the striatum can enhance dopamine production in this area of the brain. In rats and monkeys this approach has also ameliorated parkinsonian symptoms. Trials in patients have been approved and will be launched soon.

Michael Kaplitt of Cornell University and his team are taking a different tack, using gene therapy to shut down some of the brain regions that become overactive when dopamine released from the substantia nigra falls too low—including the subthalamic nucleus of the basal ganglia. (The loss of dopamine causes neurons making glutamate, an excitatory neurotransmitter, to act unopposed and thus overstimulate their targets, causing movement disorders.) Kaplitt will begin human trials using a virus to introduce the gene for glutamic acid decarboxylase—which is crucial to the production of the inhibitory neurotransmitter gamma amino butyric acid (GABA)—to these sites. He and his co-workers hope that the GABA will quell the overexcited cells and thus calm parkinsonian movement disorders. In the experiments, they thread a tube about the width of a hair through a hole the size of a quarter on top of a patient's skull. The tube delivers a dose of virus, which ferries copies of the gene into neurons of the subthalamic nucleus. The chemical released from the altered cells should not only quiet the overactive neurons residing in that region but may be dispatched to other overactive brain areas.

Perhaps the most hotly debated potential treatment entails transplanting cells to replace those that have died. The idea has been to implant embryonic stem cells or adult stem cells and to coax these undifferentiated cells into becoming dopamine-producing neurons. Because embryonic stem cells are derived from days-old embryos created during in vitro fertilization, their use is highly controversial. Fewer ethical questions surround the use of adult stem cells, which are harvested from adult tissue, but some scientists believe these cells are more difficult to work with.

Despite important progress in iden-

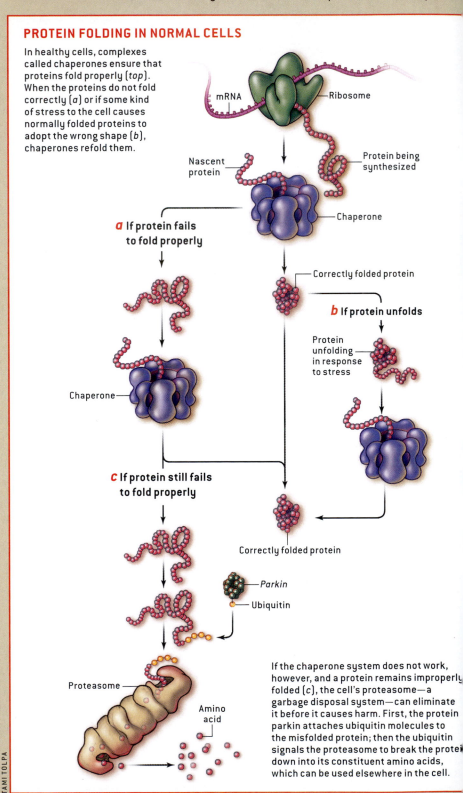

PROTEINS AND PARKINSON'S

Accumulations of misfolded proteins called Lewy bodies have been recognized for decades as hallmark of Parkinson's. Scientists do not yet know whether these protein clusters are protect

PROTEIN FOLDING IN NORMAL CELLS

In healthy cells, complexes called chaperones ensure that proteins fold properly (*top*). When the proteins do not fold correctly (*a*) or if some kind of stress to the cell causes normally folded proteins to adopt the wrong shape (*b*), chaperones refold them.

mRNA — Ribosome

Protein being synthesized

Nascent protein — Chaperone

a If protein fails to fold properly

Correctly folded protein

b If protein unfolds

Protein unfolding in response to stress

Chaperone

c If protein still fails to fold properly

Correctly folded protein

Parkin

Ubiquitin

Proteasome

Amino acid

If the chaperone system does not work, however, and a protein remains improperly folded (*c*), the cell's proteasome—a garbage disposal system—can eliminate it before it causes harm. First, the protein parkin attaches ubiquitin molecules to the misfolded protein; then the ubiquitin signals the proteasome to break the protein down into its constituent amino acids, which can be used elsewhere in the cell.

TAMI TOLPA

...ause they keep the toxic proteins out of mischief) or whether they ultimately trigger the death ...erve cells. Nevertheless, it is clear that proteins gone awry underlie this devastating disease.

WHAT GOES WRONG IN PARKINSON'S

For reasons not fully understood, the chaperone and proteasome system fail in people who become ill with Parkinson's. Misfolded proteins accumulate in cells because the chaperones cannot keep up or the proteasome system cannot break down the miscreant proteins fast enough; this buildup can damage and kill affected neurons. Recent genetic studies have suggested that mutant forms of two proteins—alpha-synuclein (*left*) and parkin (*right*)—can help undermine the chaperone and protein disposal system.

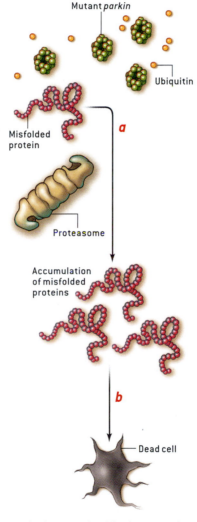

A very rare mutation in the *alpha-synuclein* gene can cause Parkinson's by giving rise to a form of the protein that resists breakdown by proteasomes (*a, above*). In a sign that Lewy bodies might sometimes be protective, groups of mutant alpha-synuclein that end up in a Lewy body (*b*) appear to be less damaging initially than copies of the protein that roam the nerve cell, causing its quick demise (*c*).

In the case of parkin, the mutated versions fail to add ubiquitin to misfolded proteins. As a result, the proteasome cannot break down the proteins (*a, above*), which ultimately cause cell death (*b*). Mutated parkin does not give rise to Lewy bodies.

...tifying the molecular cues and recipes for pushing undifferentiated cells to produce dopamine, no one yet knows whether transplantation of any kind will be as fruitful a strategy as has been hoped. The clinical trials using the most meaningful protocols have so far been conducted with fetal material. These have shown hundreds of thousands of surviving transplanted dopamine-producing cells in patients, yet the functional benefits have been at best modest and inconsistent, and the treatment has been associated with serious adverse effects, including dyskinesias (uncontrollable writhing and twisting movements). Scientists are trying to determine why transplantation has not been more helpful and why side effects have arisen, but for now they are not conducting human trials of the procedure in the U.S.

Finally, researchers continue to investigate and refine the approach behind deep-brain stimulation: applying electric pulses. Several months ago Stéphane Palfi and his colleagues at the CEA Frédéric Joliot Hospital Service in Orsay, France, reported that gently stimulating the brain surface could improve symptoms in baboons with a version of Parkinson's. Clinical trials are under way in France and elsewhere to determine whether this surgical intervention is similarly effective in humans.

Although much remains unknown about Parkinson's, the genetic and cellular insights that have come to light in just the past few years are highly encouraging. They give new hope for treatments that will combine with existing ones to slow disease progression and improve control of this distressing disorder. **SA**

MORE TO EXPLORE

Parkinson's Disease, Parts 1 and 2. A. E. Lang and A. M. Lozano in *New England Journal of Medicine,* Vol. 339, pages 1044–1053 and pages 1130–1143; October 8 and October 15, 1998.

Genetic Clues to the Pathogenesis of Parkinson's Disease. Miguel Vila and Serge Przedborski in *Nature Medicine,* Vol. 10, pages S58–S62; July 2004.

Neurodegenerative Diseases: A Decade of Discoveries Paves the Way for Therapeutic Breakthroughs. Mark S. Forman, John Q. Trojanowski and Virginia M-Y Lee in *Nature Medicine,* Vol. 10, pages 1055–1063; 2004.

THE MUTABLE BRAIN

SCORE ONE FOR BELIEVERS IN THE ADAGE "USE IT OR LOSE IT." TARGETED MENTAL AND PHYSICAL EXERCISES SEEM TO IMPROVE THE BRAIN IN UNEXPECTED WAYS

BY MARGUERITE HOLLOWAY

"THE BRAIN WAS CONSTRUCTED TO CHANGE," ASSERTS Michael M. Merzenich as he sits in a small conference room at the University of California at San Francisco Medical Center. The large windows to his left look out onto a hill thick with eucalyptus trees, their branches moving now this way, now that, in the morning's wind. Merzenich's observation—no longer so radical as it was when he and a handful of others put it forth in the 1980s—is that the brain does the same: it moves this way, then that, depending on how experience pushes it. This may seem an obvious idea: of course our brains revise themselves—we learn, after all. But Merzenich is talking about something bigger: this ability of the brain to reconfigure itself has more dramatic implications.

It is as if the brain is a vast floodplain. One year the water might run eastward in a series of small channels; the next it might cut a river deep through the center. A year later, and a map of the floodplain looks completely different: streams are meandering to the west. It is the same with a brain, the argument goes. Change the input—be it a behavior, a mental exercise, such as calculating a tip or playing a new board game, or a physical skill—

and the brain changes accordingly. Magnetic resonance imaging machines reveal the new map: different regions light up. And Merzenich and others who work in this field of neuroplasticity are not just talking about young brains, about the still developing infant or child brain, able to learn a first language and then a second in a single bound. These researchers are describing old brains, adult brains, your brain.

They are saying that the brain can be extensively remodeled throughout the course of one's life, without drugs, without surgery. Regions of the brain can be taught to do different tasks if need be. If one area has dysfunction or damage, another can step in like an understudy and play the role. Such task shifting has been reported in stroke patients who have lost speech or motor ability, cerebral palsy patients, musicians or workers who can no longer move one finger at a time, and those with obsessive-compulsive disorder or reading disorders. A series of intense mental and physical exercises have undone the effects of injury.

The next step, Merzenich and colleagues say, is to expand and refine these treatments and to investigate exercise-based tasks that can ameliorate

THE HOMUNCULUS VIEW

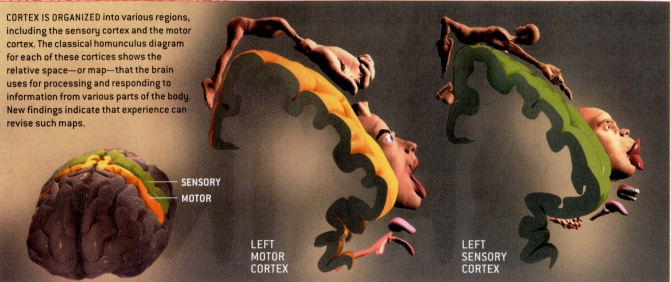

CORTEX IS ORGANIZED into various regions, including the sensory cortex and the motor cortex. The classical homunculus diagram for each of these cortices shows the relative space—or map—that the brain uses for processing and responding to information from various parts of the body. New findings indicate that experience can revise such maps.

SENSORY
MOTOR

LEFT
MOTOR
CORTEX

LEFT
SENSORY
CORTEX

schizophrenia, Parkinson's disease, the memory loss of aging, autism and a host of other problems. "One of my dreams is to find all the ways that you can use the plasticity processes of the brain to drive correction," Merzenich muses. "My belief is that this sort of thing will be part of a normal future life. It will be understood that you have to exercise your brain and that there are specific things that you have to do."

To many people—those who meditate or practice biofeedback or undergo psychotherapy—this idea may seem intuitive: focus your effort in certain ways, and your brain, as glimpsed through your behavior, will alter. Within the neuroscience and medical communities, however, this idea and its potential clinical uses are new. "If you go back to the late 1970s and the1980s, people thought of the brain as a hardwired black box," notes Thomas P. Sutula, director of the center for neuroscience at the University of Wisconsin–Madison. "This whole area is as close to a revolution in concept as you can imagine."

Yet it is a nascent revolution and one that is hard to get a handle on, perhaps in part because one of its leading figures is so difficult to pin down. Mention Merzenich's name to a neuroscientist, and he or she will most likely celebrate his brilliance and the importance of talking with him in one breath and in the next add "if you can find him." People talk of being mesmerized by his vision during a presentation, only to wonder a few days later what the data were: "Where's the beef?" asks one scientist. "He is a phantom," jokes another. Some scientists are chary of Merzenich because he started a for-profit company to develop plasticity-based therapies and feel that he has rushed to market without adequate testing.

Beyond the controversy surrounding Merzenich lie the fundamental questions of this new field. Although researchers have laid the foundation for appreciating skill-based or experience-driven neuroplasticity, there are many unknowns. The limits of it, for one. No one knows just how plastic the adult brain is as opposed to the child's—except that it is less so. No one fully understands how plasticity operates at all its various levels, from electrical pulses and neurotransmitters on up to the synapses, networks and specialized regions of the brain. And no one knows how much one part of the brain may lose when it shoulders another's burden—what the "dark side," as some researchers put it, might entail.

Of Synapses and Sections

"'PLASTICITY' IS THE MOST abused word in neuroscience," declares Roger Nicoll, whose U.C.S.F. laboratory is just across town from Merzenich's. The term has come to describe virtually any change in the brain, from the chemical level to the formation of new neurons (a process called neurogenesis) to the remapping of larger regions. At its most basic, however, it is what Nicoll studies: the plasticity of the synapse, which is the place where neurons

OVERVIEW/*Remolding the Brain*

- Contrary to long-held belief, the structure of the adult brain is not set in stone. More readily than was once thought, one region can step in and take over the function of another.
- Researchers are harnessing this neuroplasticity to treat people with reading disorders, stroke and forms of repetitive stress injury, among other conditions.
- Some scientists hope to use physical exercises and computer-based games to help individuals retrain their brains to overcome memory problems and various mental disorders.

communicate with one another by way of chemical signals, or neurotransmitters. Learning entails strengthening connections between neurons—by creating more connections between neurons as well as by enhancing their ability to communicate chemically. These changes link neurons in a chain that can be retraced to evoke a certain movement or feeling or thought, a phenomenon captured in the oft-quoted phrase "Neurons that fire together, wire together." It is at the level of the synapse that neuroplasticity lives or dies.

Until the mid-1960s it was thought that adults could not form new synapses, that the connections between neurons were frozen into position once brain development stopped. Then studies began to suggest that this was not so. For instance, researchers Geoffrey Raisman and Pauline M. Field, then at Oxford University, demonstrated that there was synaptic plasticity in adults. Others, including Mark R. Rosenzweig of the University of California at Berkeley and William T. Greenough of the University of Illinois and their colleagues, made dramatic discoveries about how environment and experience affect the brain. Greenough, for example, demonstrated that both young and mature rats could establish new synapses if they were given challenging tasks or placed in "complex environments"—which, he points out, are simply very nice cages with nice toys, "certainly not as challenging intellectually as the environment in which they are normally found." These synapses gave rise to enhanced memory and motor coordination.

These studies of exercise and what has come to be called enrichment (providing stimulation through toys or tasks) continue to flower and are being mined for their clinical applications. Stimulation and exercise speed recovery from brain injury in rats, and recent research has suggested that if mice carrying a Huntington's gene are placed in a complex setting, the development of the disease is delayed. Greenough and other investigators have connected these effects not only to the creation of synapses but to the creation of blood vessels and of brain cells called astrocytes—which are important in mopping up excess materials, such as potassium, and in maintaining an optimal environment for neurons. The formation of myelin, a lipid sheath that covers nerve axons and is crucial for their survival and effectiveness, is also enhanced in these situations.

Appreciation for plasticity at a larger scale—at the level of an entire network of neurons or a region of the brain—came well after the recognition of synaptic plasticity. It was, however, an old suggestion. In the late 1800s and early 1900s several sci-

entists had proposed that the brain was plastic, shaped by experience. William James, for example, had posited that the brain is constantly changed by experience, and in the 1920s Karl Lashley found that the motor cortex of monkeys seemed to change every week. Similar work continued through the 1970s, but the findings of scientists who felt the adult brain was fixed and unchanging predominated: the brain changed massively only during infant development and early childhood, so-called critical stages. "The religion developed from the mainstream," Merzenich notes, "and the mainstream thought that the brain was like a computer that established its critical functionality in critical periods."

People THOUGHT of THE BRAIN as a hardwired BLACK BOX.

In the 1980s a series of experiments by Merzenich and his collaborators, including Jon Kaas of Vanderbilt University, revealed that an adult monkey's motor cortex could undergo change. The cortex—the outer part of the brain where, in humans, regions for language and reasoning reside—is organized into areas for sensory, motor, auditory and other information. In one study the researchers am-

REMAPPING OF THE HAND

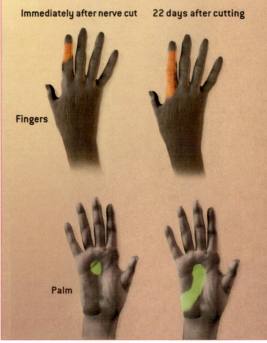

Immediately after nerve cut   22 days after cutting

Fingers

Palm

IN A NOW CLASSIC monkey experiment, Michael M. Merzenich demonstrated the plasticity of the brain's cortical maps. After he cut a nerve conveying information from a part of a finger or hand (shaded areas on left) to a specific patch of cortex, he found that the same cortical patch began responding to regions of the hand that it did not serve before (shaded areas on right). What is more, the areas represented in that cortex expanded as time went by.

putated a monkey's finger and saw that the place in the motor cortex that had been activated by that finger was soon showing responses from neurons conveying information from an adjacent finger, indicating that the brain area originally devoted to the lost finger was now monitoring and processing information from the next one. Squatters had immediately laid claim to the abandoned site. "That was an awakening to me," Merzenich reflects.

It was a revelation to the neuroscientific community at large as well. "He was one of the first to do work showing that these [neural] maps moved, and I was stunned," recalls Bryan Kolb, a leading neuroplasticity researcher at the University of Lethbridge in Canada. "People thought there was a genetic blueprint of the brain and how things were organized. No one suspected that changes could have been detected at that gross a level."

The squatters had come from right next door, though, mere millimeters away. Then, in 1991, invaders were found to travel whole centimeters. The foundations for this discovery had been laid many years earlier when Edward Taub, now at the University of Alabama at Birmingham, severed some of the nerves of one arm in a few monkeys to see what happened to their brains as a result. Taub was forced to abandon his research on the Silver Spring monkeys, as they came to be known, because of a lawsuit by animal-rights activists. For a while, his investigations came to a halt.

Years later those same monkeys were examined

Constraint-induced movement therapy works on the principle that a person can be taught to use another part of his or her brain to take over the function of a damaged or dysfunctional area. By restraining his unimpaired arm, this patient forces his brain to relearn how to use the arm affected by stroke.

by Tim P. Pons of the Wake Forest University School of Medicine, Taub and other scientists, who found something remarkable. The area of the brain that had originally received information from the now useless arm was receiving information from the face. The changes extended across great distances. "There was huge reorganization in the cortex that no one thought possible," explains Ford Ebner of Vanderbilt University. "It was another milestone." The adult brain was clearly a dynamic and efficient landlord: no empty space went unused.

Musical Maps

OVER THE PAST TWO DECADES, the research in monkeys has converged with evidence in humans, and cortical plasticity has become an accepted characteristic of the adult brain. In people who have lost a limb, studies show that the space that formerly deciphered information from that limb can serve the stump or the face. In string musicians, the area of the cortex governing the fingering hand is larger than that of the nonfingering hand, and the most-used fingers take the largest space. In Braille readers, the visual cortex becomes active as they touch their fingers to the bumps.

As all these data converged, Merzenich, Taub and others tried to figure out how to use them to benefit those with various injuries or disabilities. "We knew that the brains of children and adults are plastic throughout life," Merzenich says. "And that led us to a simple question: Can we drive changes in the brain at an older age that would be corrective?"

The strongest evidence so far that the brain can be healed by its own plasticity comes from work with stroke patients that Taub and his colleagues began in the 1980s. During earlier experiments, Taub had discovered that monkeys whose arm nerves had been severed could still move their arm if they were forced into doing so by an electric shock. It turns out that people who have lost motor function because of stroke can also learn to use their limb again. By restraining the good arm and having patients perform intensive motor tasks and training with the weak arm for many hours a day for two weeks, Taub and his co-workers—including Wolfgang Mitner of the University of Jena and Thomas Elbert of the University of Konstanz, both in Germany—forced patients to get their seemingly dead limb to move again. Such treatment is called constraint-induced (CI) movement therapy. "The traditional wisdom in the field was that after one year, there was no recovery of function," Taub explains. Yet some patients—even those whose strokes occurred 20 or more years earlier—have been able to use their arms effectively again.

CONTROL SUBJECT

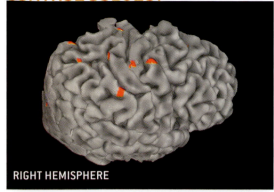

RIGHT HEMISPHERE

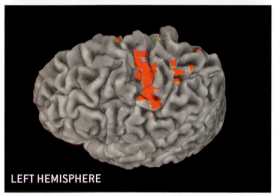

LEFT HEMISPHERE

Active brain regions (*red* and *yellow*) can be seen in these fMRI images of a control subject's two hemispheres (*left*) and those of a stroke patient (*right*). When the control subject opens and closes his right hand, the left motor cortex lights up. After rehabilitation, a stroke patient with severe left hemisphere damage uses many areas of the cortex in both the right and left hemispheres to do the same, suggesting that the brain has reorganized to allow for this movement.

STROKE PATIENT

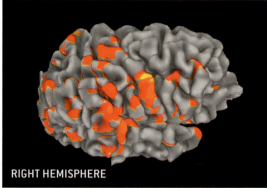

RIGHT HEMISPHERE

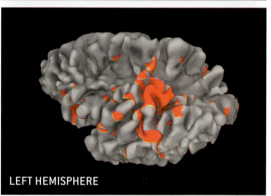

LEFT HEMISPHERE

The recovery is reflected in the shifting maps of the subjects' brains. "The CI therapy had recruited large new areas of the cortex adjacent to the damaged area," Taub points out. Other groups have seen this as well, and CI therapy is now practiced in various institutions. A recent study by Daniel B. Hier of the University of Illinois at Chicago determined that cortical patterns in stroke patients also shift after another form of rehabiliation.

Although the practice is widespread in various forms, many experts are awaiting further study before they embrace it. To this end, the National Institutes of Health has funded a six-site clinical trial of CI therapy. It will be important to get replication, notes Jordan Grafman of the National Institute of Neurological Disorders and Stroke. Investigators need to know, he says, "whether CI therapy works for some kinds of patients and not others and when after injury it should be done. You need a lot of studies."

Taub, Elbert and their colleagues have begun to use CI therapy to treat children with cerebral palsy. They have also successfully rehabilitated stroke victims who have lost their ability to speak well. These aphasic patients have repeated certain sounds for hours a day. The "constraint" in this method does not entail any "restraint," as the motor therapy does. It is essentially just intensive practice of words and sounds.

Taub and others, including Merzenich and Nan-

cy Byl of U.C.S.F., have used similar therapy to help musicians and workers recover the use of individual fingers. Sometimes when people use a series of fingers over and over again in quick succession, the distinctions between regions in the cortex begin to blur. One finger's zone melds into another's. The result is focal-hand dystonia: try to raise one finger, and another or several inevitably come along, too. By using repetitive tasks that are very distinct for each finger, the researchers say they have been able to restore the original boundaries of the map.

Merzenich has also turned his attention to language disorders and dyslexia in children—as well as some adults—and it is this research that has earned him a degree of enmity and skepticism. In the mid-1990s he joined forces with Paula Tallal of Rutgers University to form Scientific Learning, a company that produces and sells a computer-based program called Fast ForWord. The idea the two had, based on insights from their independent research, was that by slowing down certain sounds—such as "ba" and "da"—children who were having trouble processing language could quickly begin to hear the distinct sounds, the "b" separated from the "ah." Over hundreds of repetitions—training during games that can last for 20 hours a week for months—these sounds could gradually be sped up and, in time, the child would learn to hear and process the sounds at normal speed. According to a recent paper in *Proceedings of the National Acade-*

my of Sciences by Merzenich, Tallal and a group of researchers, dyslexic children participating in Fast ForWord not only improved their reading skills, but their brains changed—different regions were processing language.

Although some researchers believe that this technique might well prove itself, they await independent reviews and replication before they are convinced. Guinevere F. Eden of Georgetown University Medical Center notes that there have been no controlled studies of reading improvements: the kids with reading problems who received the intervention have not been compared with another set of dyslexics who did not. "You would expect kids to be better on the second round of a task because they are always better on the second test—even if nontrained," Eden observes, adding that computer-based games often increase players' attention, so improvement might have more to do with attentiveness as opposed to language processing. And she worries that parents will develop hopes that won't be realized or will spend too much money purchasing the software: "It is a very vulnerable group, and it is a pity that the system isn't in place to protect them more."

Merzenich dismisses these criticisms, scoffing at the idea that the studies he is a party to—such as the recent one in *PNAS*—could be biased. And he says he has no regrets about forming Scientific Learning, except that the programs have not yet reached as many kids as he would have hoped. For some in the field, this business interest has tarnished Merzenich's accomplishments; his research will always be colored by commercial interest. But others applaud it. "It is great to go sit in your lab, but better for people to act," Sutula says. "You can make people's lives better."

And the company offered a practical solution for one of the principal problems of the field of applied neuroplasticity: the gulf between the neuroscience and the rehabilitation communities. "There is a lot of interesting knowledge about how to improve function in people," Grafman notes. "But translating that into rehabilitation has been painful and slow."

"It is very important that the research get carried out, and it is almost impossible to get funding to do this," Taub agrees. To the rehabilitation community, several of these ideas "seem out of left

Reading program designed by Michael M. Merzenich and Paula Tallal seeks to rewire the brains of children with dyslexia or other problems. The controversial computer-based strategy, called Fast ForWord, has not been independently assessed so far, but the researchers say they have found significant improvement in children's reading comprehension.

field," he says. "Although from the point of view of neuroscience, it is absolutely straightforward."

Limits of Plasticity

MERZENICH'S CURRENT preoccupation may seem even further afield. He is investigating whether training and games can reverse or ameliorate schizophrenia, autism and the memory loss that can accompany aging. As yet, there are no published data to turn to. And Merzenich is not forthcoming about his collaborators either. Although he granted a long interview and opened up his lab, Merzenich never responded to my requests for further information—despite his promises to provide names and despite myriad follow-up phone calls and e-mail messages.

But if his idea bears fruit, it will be stunning. Merzenich believes that the neurotransmitters that underlie memory can be bolstered during tasks performed while sitting at a computer. "Just as in kids that are having problems with learning and memory and whatever," he argues, "the machinery is plastic. And you can almost certainly drive positive changes in the brains of elderly individuals by engaging that machine." He says he can discuss results soon and that the same principle will apply—and is already working—for autistic patients and people with Parkinson's disease. "We are overwhelmingly dominated by thinking that we are going to fix everything in the brain by drug manipulation or by some change in the status of the physical structure of the brain, because it is deteriorating," he asserts. "But a computer-directed exercise can be very efficient. Because it can pound your brain in a highly controlled way." For example, patients could play a computer game in which they won money or overcame obstacles; the positive reward could trigger the release of, say, dopamine—a neurotransmitter associated with the experience of pleasure and one that is also progressively lost in certain illnesses, such as Parkinson's.

Researchers are waiting to see the beef. And to understand what the limits of plasticity are. "My fundamental concern about Mike's view is that he doesn't take the role of genes as seriously as the data suggest," says Steven E. Hyman of Harvard University. "He is a brilliant zealot for plasticity—we need his voice. But ultimately I fear our brain may not turn out to be as plastic." Others wonder what the costs might be—for instance, could triggering plasticity at some point diminish the brain's ability to flourish later on?—and how drugs could be combined with an understanding of neuroplasticity to get fuller recovery. "The sky's the limit, and we are trying to figure out the rules," Kolb states.

In the meantime, evidence from other quarters seems to bolster Merzenich's fundamental belief that healing plasticity can be driven by behavior. Jeffrey Schwartz of the University of California at Irvine has reported brain remapping in people with obsessive compulsive disorder who have undergone behavioral training. They have apparently remolded their brain to avoid certain patterns of thinking. Researchers at Laval University's Geriatric Research Unit in Quebec have suggested that exercise is protective against the development of Alzheimer's disease. A study last year in the *Journal of the American Medical Association* indicated that mental activity, such as reading the newspaper every day,

THE SKY'S THE LIMIT, and we are trying to figure out the rules.

could keep Alzheimer's at bay; a large-scale federal study came to the same conclusion.

And during the eight years after his riding accident, actor Christopher Reeve has apparently exercised himself out of paraplegia into a state where he can move his fingers and toes and push with his legs. His recovery marks the first time such extensive reconnection of the spinal cord to the brain has been recorded after such a long period. His brain lights up in unexpected places. "The nervous system is capable of doing all sorts of things," declares Reeve's physician, John W. McDonald of the Washington University School of Medicine. As for fixing the brain, he says, "We just don't know yet which kinds of mental tasks can correct which problems." Merzenich would probably say he knows—if you could get him on the phone. ⬛

Marguerite Holloway is a contributing editor at Scientific American *and a science writer based in New York City.*

MORE TO EXPLORE

Neural Plasticity: Merzenich, Taub and Greenough. Erin Clifford in *Harvard Brain*, Vol. 16, pages 16–20; 1999. Available online at http://hcs.harvard.edu/~husn/BRAIN/vol6/p16-20-Neuronalplasticity.pdf

Cortical Reorganization of Function after Brain Damage. Edited by Harvey S. Levin and Jordan Grafman. Oxford University Press, 2000.

Neural Consequences of Environmental Enrichment. Henriette van Praag, Gerd Kempermann and Fred H. Gage in *Nature Reviews Neuroscience,* Vol. 1, No. 3, pages 191–198; December 2000.

Exercise, Experience and the Aging Brain. James D. Churchill, Roberto Galves, Stanley Colcombe, Rodney A. Swain, Arthur F. Kramer and William T. Greenough in *Neurobiology of Aging,* Vol. 23, No. 5, pages 941–955; September 2002.

The Mind and the Brain: Neuroplasticity and the Power of Mental Force. Jeffrey M. Schwartz and Sharon Begley. Harper Collins, 2002.

BEHAVIORAL CHANGES accompany motherhood in virtually all female mammals. New research suggests that hormone-induced alterations of the female brain may make mothers more vigilant, nurturing and attuned to the needs of their young, as well as improve their spatial memory and learning.

THE MATERNAL BRAIN

Pregnancy and motherhood change the structure of the female mammal's brain, making mothers attentive to their young and better at caring for them

By CRAIG HOWARD KINSLEY and KELLY G. LAMBERT

Mothers are made, not born. Virtually all female mammals, from rats to monkeys to humans, undergo fundamental behavioral changes during pregnancy and motherhood. What was once a largely self-directed organism devoted to its own needs and survival becomes one focused on the care and well-being of its offspring. Although scientists have long observed and marveled at this transition, only now are they beginning to understand what causes it. New research indicates that the dramatic hormonal fluctuations that occur during pregnancy, birth and lactation may remodel the female brain, increasing the size of neurons in some regions and producing structural changes in others.

Some of these sites are involved in regulating maternal behaviors such as building nests, grooming young and protecting them from predators. Other affected regions, though, control memory, learning, and responses to fear and stress. Recent experiments have shown that mother rats outperform virgins in navigating mazes and capturing prey. In addition to motivating females toward caring for their offspring, the hormone-induced brain changes may enhance a mother rat's foraging

abilities, giving her pups a better chance of survival. What is more, the cognitive benefits appear to be long-lasting, persisting until the mother rats enter old age.

Although studies of this phenomenon have so far focused on rodents, it is likely that human females also gain long-lasting mental benefits from motherhood. Most mammals share similar maternal behaviors, which are probably controlled by the same brain regions in both humans and rats. In fact, some researchers have suggested that the development of maternal behavior was one of the main drivers for the evolution of the mammalian brain. As mammals arose from their reptile forebears, their reproductive strategy shifted from drop-the-eggs-and-flee to defend-the-nest, and the selective advantages of the latter approach may have favored the emergence of hormonal brain changes and the resulting beneficial behaviors. The hand—or paw—that rocks the cradle indeed rules the world.

Awash in Hormones

HALF A CENTURY AGO scientists found the first hints that the hormones of pregnancy spur a female mammal's ardor for

its offspring. Starting in the 1940s, Frank A. Beach of Yale University showed that estrogen and progesterone, the female reproductive hormones, regulate responses such as aggression and sexuality in rats, hamsters, cats and dogs. Further pioneering work by Daniel S. Lehrman and Jay S. Rosenblatt, then at the Institute of Animal Behavior at Rutgers University, demonstrated that the same hormones were required for the display of maternal behavior in rats. In 1984 Robert S. Bridges, now at the Tufts Cummings School of Veterinary Medicine, reported that the production of estrogen and progesterone increased at certain points during pregnancy and that the appearance of maternal behavior depended on the interplay of the hormones and their eventual decrease. Bridges and his colleagues went on to show that prolactin, the lactation-inducing hormone, stimulated maternal behavior in female rats already primed with progesterone and estrogen.

Besides hormones, other chemicals affecting the nervous system appear to play a role in triggering motherly impulses. In 1980 Alan R. Gintzler of the State University of New York

also involved [see box on opposite page], and each of these sites is rife with receptors for hormones and other neurochemicals. Noted neuroscientist Paul MacLean of the National Institute of Mental Health has proposed that the neural pathways from the thalamus, the brain's relay station, to the cingulate cortex, which regulates emotions, are an important part of the maternal behavior system. Damaging the cingulate cortex in mother rats eliminates their maternal behavior. In his 1990 book *The Triune Brain in Evolution*, MacLean hypothesized that the development of these pathways helped to shape the mammalian brain as it evolved from the simpler reptilian brain.

Interestingly, once the reproductive hormones initiate the maternal response, the brain's dependency on them seems to diminish, and the offspring alone can stimulate maternal behavior. Although a newly born mammal is a demanding little creature, unappealing on many levels—it is smelly, helpless and sleeps only intermittently—the mother's devotion to it is the most motivated of all animal displays, exceeding even sexual behavior and feeding. Joan I. Morrell of Rutgers has sug-

When given the choice between cocaine and newly born pups, mother rats choose pups.

Downstate Medical Center reported increases in endorphins—painkilling proteins produced by the pituitary gland and the brain region called the hypothalamus—over the course of a rat's pregnancy, especially just before birth. In addition to preparing the mother for the discomfort of birth, the endorphins may initiate maternal behavior. Taken together, the data demonstrate that the regulation of this behavior requires the coordination of many hormonal and neurochemical systems and that the female brain is exquisitely responsive to the changes that occur with pregnancy.

Scientists have also identified the brain regions that govern maternal behavior. Michael Numan and Marilyn Numan of Boston College have shown that a part of the hypothalamus in the female brain, the medial preoptic area (mPOA), is largely responsible for this activity; creating a lesion in the mPOA or injecting morphine into the region will disrupt the characteristic behavior of mother rats. But other areas of the brain are

gested that the offspring themselves may be the reward that reinforces maternal behavior. When given the choice between cocaine and newly born pups, mother rats choose pups.

Craig Ferris of the University of Massachusetts Medical School recently studied the brains of lactating mother rats using functional magnetic resonance imaging (fMRI), a noninvasive technique that tracks changes in brain activity. Ferris found that activity in the mother's nucleus accumbens, a site that is integral to reinforcement and reward, increased significantly when she nursed her pups. And Ronald J. Gandelman of Rutgers has shown that when a mother mouse is given the opportunity to receive foster pups—the mouse presses a bar in her cage, causing the pups to slide down a chute—the mother will keep pressing the bar until her cage fills with the squirming, pink objects.

Several researchers have hypothesized that as suckling pups attach to their mother's nipples, they may release tiny amounts of endorphins in the mother's body. These natural painkillers may act somewhat like an opiate drug, drawing the mother again and again to contact with her pups. Suckling and pup contact also release the hormone oxytocin, which may have a similar effect on the mother. Lower mammalian species such as mice and rats, which most likely lack the lofty principles and motivations of humans, may care for their pups for the simple reason that it feels good to do so.

But what about the motivations of the human mother? Jeffrey P. Lorberbaum of the Medical University of South Carolina has used fMRI to examine the brains of human moms as they listened to their babies cry. The patterns of activity were similar to those of the rodent mothers, with the mPOA region

Overview/*Mother Wit*

- Studies of rodents have shown that the hormones of pregnancy trigger changes not only in the brain regions governing maternal behavior but also in areas that regulate memory and learning.
- These brain changes may explain why mother rats are better than virgins at navigating mazes and capturing prey.
- Researchers are now investigating whether human females also gain mental benefits from motherhood.

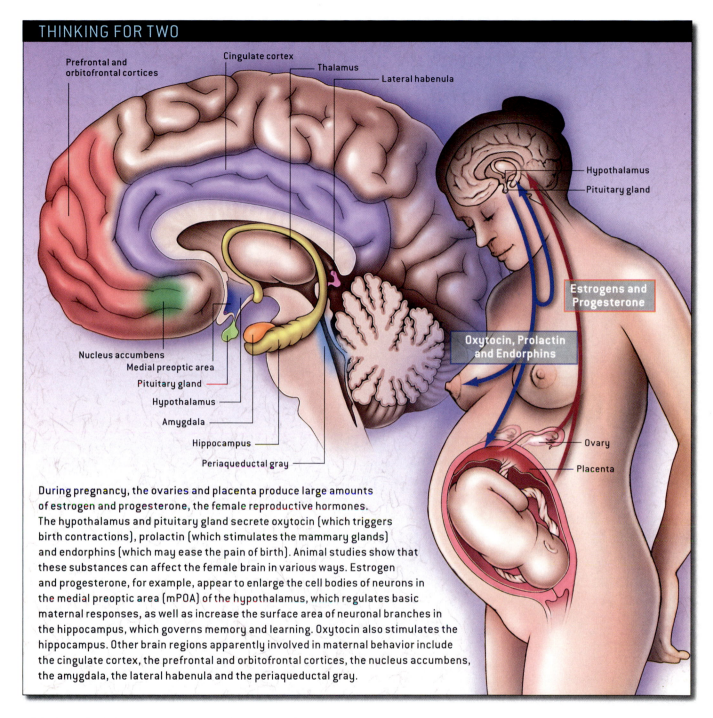

Prefrontal and orbitofrontal cortices

Cingulate cortex

Thalamus

Lateral habenula

Hypothalamus

Pituitary gland

Estrogens and Progesterone

Oxytocin, Prolactin and Endorphins

Nucleus accumbens

Medial preoptic area

Pituitary gland

Hypothalamus

Amygdala

Hippocampus

Periaqueductal gray

Ovary

Placenta

During pregnancy, the ovaries and placenta produce large amounts of estrogen and progesterone, the female reproductive hormones. The hypothalamus and pituitary gland secrete oxytocin (which triggers birth contractions), prolactin (which stimulates the mammary glands) and endorphins (which may ease the pain of birth). Animal studies show that these substances can affect the female brain in various ways. Estrogen and progesterone, for example, appear to enlarge the cell bodies of neurons in the medial preoptic area (mPOA) of the hypothalamus, which regulates basic maternal responses, as well as increase the surface area of neuronal branches in the hippocampus, which governs memory and learning. Oxytocin also stimulates the hippocampus. Other brain regions apparently involved in maternal behavior include the cingulate cortex, the prefrontal and orbitofrontal cortices, the nucleus accumbens, the amygdala, the lateral habenula and the periaqueductal gray.

of the hypothalamus and the prefrontal and orbitofrontal cortices all lighting up. Furthermore, Andreas Bartels and Semir Zeki of University College London found that the brain areas that regulate reward became activated when human moms merely gazed at their children. The similarity between the human and rodent responses suggests the existence of a general maternal circuit in the mammalian brain.

Brain Changes

TO UNDERSTAND THE WORKINGS of this circuit, researchers have studied how the female brain changes at different reproductive stages. In the 1970s Marian C. Diamond of the University of California, Berkeley, provided some of the earliest evidence while investigating the cortices of pregnant rats. The outermost layer of the brain, the cortex receives and processes sensory information and also controls voluntary movements. Rats raised in enriched sensory environments, surrounded by wheels, toys and tunnels, typically develop more intricately folded cortices than rats housed in bare cages. Diamond, however, found that the cortices of pregnant rats from impoverished environments were just as complex as those of the female rats from enriched settings. She concluded that some combination of hormones and fetus-related factors were most likely stimulating the pregnant rats' brains.

Two decades later, after studies demonstrated the importance of the mPOA to maternal behavior, investigators began looking for changes to that brain region. In the mid-1990s Lori Keyser, a researcher in one of our laboratories (Kinsley's) at the University of Richmond, showed that the cell bodies of the neurons in the mPOA of pregnant rats increase in volume. What is more, the length and number of dendrites (the signal-receiving branches extending from the cell body) in mPOA neurons increase as the pregnancy progresses. The same changes were also observed in female rats treated with a pregnancy-mimicking regimen of progesterone and estradiol, the most powerful of the natural estrogens. These neuronal alterations typically accompany a rise in protein synthesis and activity. In essence, the hormones of pregnancy "rev up" the mPOA neurons in anticipation of birth and the demands of motherhood. The nerve cells are like thoroughbreds straining at the starting gate, awaiting their release for the race. After birth, the mPOA neurons direct the mother's attention and motivation to her offspring, enabling her to care for, protect and nurture her progeny with the panoply of behaviors known collectively as maternal.

Maternal behavior encompasses many facets beyond the direct care of offspring, however, so it occurred to us that other brain regions might also undergo changes. For instance,

Are other features of the mothers' hunting skills also enhanced? Recent work by undergraduates Naomi Hester, Natalie Karp and Angela Orthmeyer in Kinsley's lab has shown that mother rats are faster than virgins at capturing prey. Slightly food-deprived mother and virgin rats were each placed in a five-foot-square enclosure bedded with wood chips, in which a cricket was hidden. The virgins took an average of nearly 270 seconds to find the cricket and eat it, compared with just more than 50 seconds for the lactating females. Even when the virgin females were made hungrier or when the sounds of the crickets were masked, the mother rats were still able to get to the prey more quickly.

Regarding the second prediction, Inga Neumann of the University of Regensburg in Germany has repeatedly documented that pregnant and lactating rats suffer less fear and anxiety (as measured by levels of stress hormones in their blood) than virgin rats when confronted with challenges such as forced swimming. Jennifer Wartella, while in Kinsley's lab, confirmed and extended these results by examining rat behavior in the five-foot-square enclosure; she found that mother rats were more likely to investigate the space and less likely to

It appears that hormonal fluctuations
ramp up neural activity during pregnancy.

a mother rat has to take risks to tend her nest and young. She must frequently leave the relative safety of the nest to forage for food, making herself and her helpless offspring more vulnerable to predators, because if she stays in the nest, she and her brood will slowly starve. We can predict two cognitive changes that would improve the mother rat's cost-benefit ratio. First, an enhancement of her foraging skills—for example, the spatial ability used for navigating her environment—would minimize the amount of time she is away from the nest. Second, a diminution of the rat's fear and anxiety would make it easier for her to leave the nest, allow her to forage faster, and steel her for confrontations with her hostile surroundings.

In 1999 we found support for the first prediction by showing that reproductive experience enhanced spatial learning and memory in rats. Young females that had experienced one or two pregnancies were much better than age-matched virgin rats at remembering the location of a food reward in two different kinds of mazes: an eight-arm radial maze [see top illustration in box on page 40] and a dry-land version of the Morris water maze, a large, circular enclosure with nine baited food wells. The improved foraging abilities were observed in both lactating females and mothers at least two weeks removed from weaning their young. Furthermore, virgin females provided with foster young performed similarly to lactating females. This result suggests that simply the presence of offspring can provide a boost to spatial memory, perhaps by stimulating brain activities that alter neuronal structures or by prompting the secretion of oxytocin.

freeze up, two hallmarks of boldness. In addition, we found a reduction in neuronal activity in the CA3 region of the hippocampus and the basolateral amygdala, two areas of the brain that regulate stress and emotion. The resulting mitigation of fear and stress responses, combined with the enhancements in spatial ability, ensures that the mother rat is able to leave the security of the nest, forage efficiently and return home quickly to care for her vulnerable offspring.

Alterations of the hippocampus, which regulates memory and learning as well as emotions, appear to play a major role in causing these behavioral changes. Some fascinating work by Catherine Woolley and Bruce McEwen of the Rockefeller University showed ebb-and-flow variations in the CA1 region of the hippocampus during a female rat's estrous cycle (the equivalent of the human menstrual cycle). The density of dendritic spines—tiny, thornlike projections that provide more surface area for the reception of nerve signals—increased in this region as the female's levels of estrogen rose. If the relatively brief hormonal fluctuations of the estrous cycle produced such striking structural changes, we wondered, what would happen to the hippocampus during pregnancy, when estrogen and progesterone levels remain high for an extended period? Graciela Stafisso-Sandoz, Regina Trainer and Princy Quadros in Kinsley's lab examined the brains of rats in the late stages of pregnancy, as well as females treated with pregnancy hormones, and found the concentrations of CA1 spines to be denser than normal. Because these spines direct input to their associated neurons, the big rise in density during pregnancy

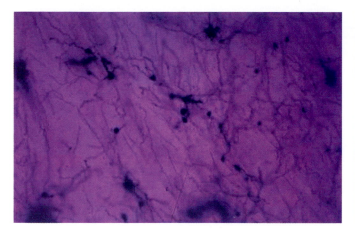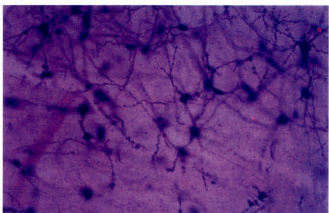

CELL BODIES of neurons from the mPOA of a virgin female rat (*left*) are much smaller than those from a pregnant rat (*right*). The hormones of pregnancy appear to "rev up" the mPOA neurons, boosting their protein synthesis and activity in anticipation of the demands of motherhood.

may contribute to the enhanced ability of the mothers to navigate mazes and capture prey.

Oxytocin, the hormone that triggers birth contractions and milk release, also appears to have effects on the hippocampus that improve memory and learning. Kazuhito Tomizawa and his colleagues at Okayama University in Japan have reported that oxytocin promotes the establishment of long-lasting connections between neurons in the hippocampus. Injections of oxytocin into the brains of virgin female mice improved their long-term memory, presumably by increasing enzyme activity that strengthened the neuronal connections. Conversely, injecting oxytocin inhibitors into the brains of mother rats impaired their performance on memory-related tasks.

Other researchers have focused on motherhood's effects on glial cells, the connective tissue of the central nervous system. Gordon W. Gifford and student collaborators in Kinsley's lab have examined astrocytes, star-shaped glial cells that provide nutrients and structural support for neurons. They found that the astrocytes in the mPOA and hippocampus of late-pregnant, lactating and hormone-treated female rats were significantly more complex and numerous than those in virgin rats. Again, it appears that hormonal fluctuations ramp up neural activity during pregnancy, modifying neurons and glial cells in critical brain regions to enhance learning and spatial memory.

Do any of these cognitive benefits extend beyond the lactational period? Jessica D. Gatewood, working with other students in Kinsley's lab, has reported that mother rats up to two years old—equivalent to human females older than 60—learn spatial tasks significantly faster than age-matched virgin rats and exhibit less steep memory declines. At every age tested (six, 12, 18 and 24 months), the mothers were better than the virgins at remembering the locations of food rewards in mazes. And when we examined the brains of the mother rats at the conclusion of testing, we found fewer deposits of amyloid precursor proteins—which seem to play a role in the degeneration of the aging nervous system—in two parts of the hippocampus, the CA1 region and the dentate gyrus.

Recent work by Gennifer Love, Ilan M. McNamara and Melissa Morgan in our other lab (Lambert's), employing a different strain of rat and testing conditions, has confirmed that long-term spatial learning is enhanced in older mother rats. What is more, the investigators gauged the boldness of the rats using a maze shaped like a plus sign, with two open arms that rodents typically avoid because they are elevated and exposed, offering no hiding places [*see bottom illustration in box on next page*]. At most of the ages through 22 months that were tested, the mother rats spent more time in the fear-evoking open arms of the maze than the virgin rats did. When the brains of the mother rats were examined, researchers found fewer degenerating cells in the cingulate, frontal and parietal cortices, regions that receive considerable sensory input. These results suggest that the repeated inundation of the female brain with the hormones of pregnancy, coupled with the enriching sensory environment of the nest, may mitigate some of the effects of aging on cognition.

The Human Connection

DO HUMAN FEMALES RECEIVE any similar cognitive benefits from pregnancy and motherhood? Recent studies indicate that the human brain may undergo changes in sensory regulatory systems that parallel the alterations in other animals. Alison Fleming of the University of Toronto at Mississauga has shown that human mothers are capable of recognizing many of their infants' odors and sounds, possibly because of enhanced sensory abilities. She and her colleagues found that mothers with high postbirth levels of the hormone cortisol were more attracted to and motivated by their babies' scents and were better able to recognize their infants' cries. The results indicate that cortisol, which typically rises with stress and

THE AUTHORS

CRAIG HOWARD KINSLEY and *KELLY G. LAMBERT* have spent more than a decade investigating the effects of pregnancy and motherhood on the female brain. Kinsley is MacEldin Trawick Professor of Neuroscience in the department of psychology and Center for Neuroscience at the University of Richmond. Lambert is professor of behavioral neuroscience and psychology, chair of the department of psychology and co-director of the Office of Undergraduate Research at Randolph-Macon College.

Recent experiments indicate that reproductive experience enhances spatial learning and memory in rats while alleviating fear and stress. These behavioral changes can improve a mother rat's foraging abilities, giving her pups a better chance of survival.

EIGHT-ARM RADIAL MAZE

First the researchers familiarized the rats with a radial maze in which food baits were initially placed in all eight arms, then in only four, then in two, and finally in just one. Then the investigators measured how well the rats remembered which arm remained baited. Mother rats who had experienced two or more pregnancies were mostly successful in completing the maze (that is, finding the bait within three minutes) from the first day of testing; the virgin female rats did not match their success until the seventh day.

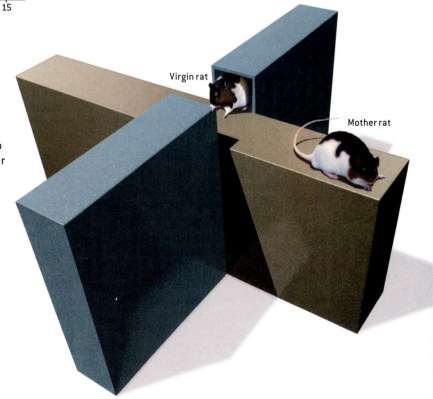

Mother rat

Virgin rat

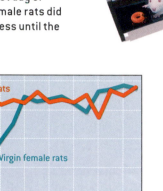

ELEVATED PLUS MAZE

In this maze, which was shaped like a plus sign and raised four feet above the floor, researchers measured how much time the rats spent in the two open arms, which rodents tend to avoid because they are elevated and exposed (unlike the maze's two closed arms). At nearly every age, the mother rats were bolder than the virgins, spending more time in the fear-evoking open arms.

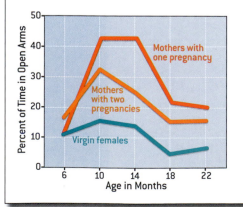

Virgin rat

Mother rat

can have a negative impact on health, may have a positive effect in new mothers. By raising cortisol levels, the stress of parenting may boost attention, vigilance and sensitivity, strengthening the mother-infant bond.

Other studies have pointed to a possible long-term effect of motherhood. As part of the New England Centenarian Study, Thomas Perls and his colleagues at Boston University found that women who had been pregnant at or after the age of 40 were four times more likely to survive to 100 than women who had been pregnant earlier in life. Perls interpreted the data to suggest that women who became pregnant naturally in their 40s were probably aging at a slower pace. We would add, however, that pregnancy and the subsequent maternal experience may have enhanced the women's brains at a crucial period when the menopause-induced decline in reproductive hormones was just starting. The cognitive benefits of motherhood may have

Animal studies show that mother rats are particularly good at multitasking. Experiments in Lambert's lab have demonstrated that mother rats nearly always beat virgins in competitions that involve simultaneously monitoring sights, sounds, odors and other animals. In a race to find a preferred food (Froot Loops), rats who had experienced two or more pregnancies were the first to attain the treat 60 percent of the time. Rats who had given birth just once won the prize 33 percent of the time, compared with only 7 percent for the virgin rats.

Finally, what about the paternal brain? Do fathers who care for offspring gain any mental benefits? Studies of the common marmoset, a small Brazilian monkey, may provide some insights. Marmosets are monogamous, and both parents participate in the care of their offspring. In collaboration with Sian Evans and V. Jessica Capri of Monkey Jungle in Miami, Fla., Anne Garrett from Lambert's lab tested mother and father mar-

Mother rats nearly always beat virgins in competitions that involve multitasking.

helped offset the loss of the memory-protecting hormones, leading to better neural health and increased longevity.

Is it possible that motherhood provides an edge to women as they compete with others for limited resources? Unfortunately, scientists have conducted little research comparing the learning or spatial memory abilities of human mothers and nonmothers. A 1999 study led by J. Galen Buckwalter of the University of Southern California showed that pregnant women had below-normal results on several verbal memory tests but that their scores rebounded soon after they gave birth. This study, however, was small (only 19 subjects) and found no significant changes in general intelligence. In her book *The Mommy Brain*, journalist Katherine Ellison documents many instances wherein the skills acquired through parenting might also aid women in the workplace. Successful leadership requires sensitivity to employee needs and a sustained vigilance of impending challenges and threats. But can these skills transfer from the nursery to the boardroom?

Investigators have begun to focus on one skill that is traditionally associated with motherhood: the ability to multitask. Do changes in the maternal brain allow mothers to balance competing demands—child care, work, social obligations and so on—better than nonmothers? Scientists do not yet know the answer, but studies indicate that the human brain is remarkably plastic: its structure and activity can change when a person is confronted with a challenge. Arne May and colleagues at the University of Regensburg found structural changes in the brains of young women and men who had learned how to juggle three balls in the air; the regions devoted to perception and the prediction of movement expanded after the subjects learned how to juggle, then contracted after they stopped practicing. Likewise, perhaps alterations occurring in the maternal brain enable the mother to juggle the demands of parenthood successfully.

mosets on a "foraging tree" in which the monkeys had to learn which containers held the most food. Parents—both mothers and fathers—outperformed nonparents in the test. This result supported earlier studies that examined a mouse species (*Peromyscus californicus*) in which the male contributes significantly to parental care. In Lambert's lab, Erica Glasper and other students found that father mice, like mothers, had an advantage in the dry-land maze; Ashley Everette and Kelly Tu showed that the fathers were quicker to investigate novel stimuli, such as Lego blocks, than their bachelor counterparts were.

In summary, reproductive experience appears to promote changes in the mammalian brain that alter skills and behavior, particularly among females. For the female, the greatest challenge from an evolutionary perspective is to ensure that her genetic investment flourishes. Maternal behaviors have evolved to increase the female's chances of success. This does not mean that mothers are better than their virgin counterparts at every task; in all likelihood, only the behaviors affecting the survival of their offspring would be enhanced. Still, many benefits seem to emerge from motherhood as the maternal brain rises to the reproductive challenge placed before it. In other words, when the going gets tough, the brain gets going. ◼

MORE TO EXPLORE

Mother Nature: Maternal Instincts and How They Shape the Human Species. Sarah B. Hrdy. Ballantine Books, 2000.

The Maternal Brain: Neurobiological and Neuroendocrine Adaptation and Disorders in Pregnancy and Post Partum. Edited by J. A. Russell, A. J. Douglas, R. J. Windle and C. D. Ingram. Elsevier, 2001.

A Tribute to Paul MacLean: The Neurobiological Relevance of Social Behavior. Edited by K. G. Lambert and R. T. Gerlai. Special issue of *Physiology and Behavior*, Vol. 79, No. 3; August 2003.

The Neurobiology of Parental Behavior. Michael Numan and Thomas R. Insel. Springer-Verlag, 2003.

Lighten

Up

SEASONAL AFFECTIVE DISORDER—THE WINTER BLUES—CAN BE LIFTED WITH BRIGHT LIGHT, AS LONG AS TREATMENT IS TIMED PROPERLY BY ULRICH KRAFT

Autumn. Mornings are dark. Dusk comes dishearteningly early. You are feeling more tired, melancholy. The rapidly disappearing daylight seems almost to drag away part of your spirit with it. Should this dip in humor worry you? Not really—you'll adjust. Unless you are prone to seasonal affective disorder. For the several million Americans who succumb, the darker half of the year brings a heavy veil of sadness. They become depressed, listless, chronically fatigued, and their mood does not rebound until March, when the daylight extends to early evening.

In general, the farther north one lives on the globe the more common seasonal depression becomes. Below the 30th parallel, which links Jacksonville, Fla., to Houston and the Baja Peninsula south of San Diego, the winter blues are virtually unknown. In sunny Florida, just 1 percent of the population suffers from seasonal affective disorder, appropriately known as SAD, but in New York State the rate is 5 percent. In Alaska, one out of every 10 residents experiences winter mood problems.

Why are some people bowled over, whereas their neighbors simply feel a bit glum? And how can all of us brighten our autumnal outlook? Psychologists and neuroscientists are finding answers. And what they are discovering goes far beyond antidotes for seasonal depression; they are gaining insight into how our environments influence our minds, how our brains control mood and how our internal clocks keep many bodily functions in sync.

Sad yet Hungry

Seasonal depression has been recognized for millennia. The great Greek physician Hippocrates was aware in the fifth century B.C. that mood and energy varied with sunlight. People living in sunnier regions were happier, had a more optimistic outlook and were less often sick, he wrote in his treatise *Airs, Waters, Places*. Yet it was not until the middle of the 20th century that people began to pay real attention to the condition. And it was not until the 1980s that researchers began to examine winter depression closely. Norman E. Rosenthal and Thomas A. Wehr, then at the National Institute of Mental Health (NIMH), and their colleagues developed diagnostic criteria that allowed them to evaluate symptoms objectively. In 1984 the malady was finally christened seasonal affective disorder.

The classic signs include diminished pleasure in life, a gloomy mood and difficulty concentrating. In the morning, SAD sufferers say they feel "good enough," but their liveliness fades with the day's passage. Week by week, as the nights lengthen, these individuals withdraw from social life, lose interest in sex and muster little enthusiasm for anything. They describe themselves as empty.

All these symptoms are common to depression, too. The difference is the seasonal link. SAD

GINTER Bilderberg/Aurora (*preceding pages*): SAMUEL VELASCO (*these two pages*)

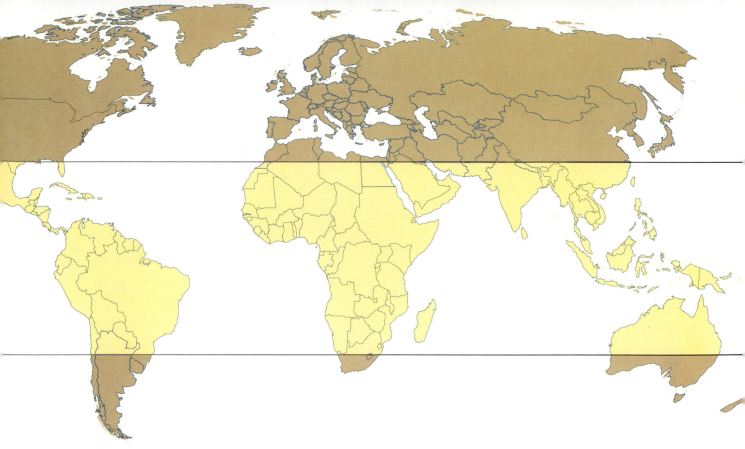

always commences at a particular time of year. "Some people have symptoms as early as September 1, but the problem is really significant in October and November," explains Siegfried Kasper, a psychiatrist at the Medical University of Vienna in Austria. In spring the problem disappears completely, as if it had never existed. Furthermore, whereas depressives often lie awake at night for hours, SAD people tend to sleep excessively, as much as four hours more a night than in summer. They seldom experience lack of appetite, common in depression, and often have hunger attacks that they satisfy with carbohydrates or sweets, leading to weight gain.

Hormone of the Night

The persistence of SAD is clear, but why would a simple absence of daylight trigger such emotional changes? Is the amount of sunlight even the critical factor? For SAD individuals, spending a long time in a windowless room can set off a depressive episode. The answer lies in how humans detect light. Many animals track the seasons by noting changes in day length. Bats, hamsters and groundhogs use the signal to go into hibernation. Daily and seasonal changes in daylight must somehow be registered by the eyes and calculated by the brain. In the early 1970s a small bundle of neurons was discovered that performed this analysis. The bundle—the size of a grain of rice—is the suprachiasmatic nucleus

(SCN), and it is located in the brain's hypothalamus near where the two optic nerves from the eyes cross [*see illustration on page 47*].

The SCN is our body's master timekeeper, our internal 24-hour clock. If this pinch of cells is removed from rats, many processes driven by normal circadian rhythm collapse, including the animals' sleep-wake cycle as well as functions of their heart, intestines and liver. As soon as the first rays of sun at dawn sneak between the eyelids onto the retina, special photoreceptor cells signal the neurons of the SCN to begin firing more rapidly. The SCN maintains this rate all day, like a signaling beacon that doesn't stop. The "ringing"—via many intermediate steps—suppresses the secretion of melatonin, the so-called sleep hormone, by the pineal gland. An evening rise of melatonin in the bloodstream makes us sleepy, and high levels prevail all night long; during the day, however, the hormone can scarcely be detected.

Melatonin's ebb and flow repeats every day. But the cycle's precise timing and duration varies across the year. In spring and summer the SCN neurons fire for longer each day; shorter signaling occurs during autumn and winter. As a result, the profile of melatonin synthesis differs for each season, and it affects many aspects of animals' lives, among them appetite, total daily activity levels, social contact, drive to reproduce and, of course, the need for sleep.

Those daily and seasonal levels of melatonin

Between the 30th parallels (*yellow area*), winter depression is almost unknown. Beyond them, rates of the ailment generally increase toward the poles—for example, from 1 percent in northern Florida to 10 percent in Alaska.

might hold the key to SAD, Thomas Wehr of the NIMH realized during his work in the 1980s. Wehr wondered whether the daily profile of melatonin production somehow differed for SAD sufferers. After tracking many subjects, Wehr found that the seasonal variation in melatonin secretion was similar for SAD and non-SAD people. But for SAD subjects the nightly melatonin cycle lasted 38 minutes longer in winter.

A 38-minute disparity might seem insignificant, given that daylight on a June day in the U.S. lasts nearly 16 hours and that even on a December day it ekes out a little more than eight hours. But the difference matters tremendously. In hamsters, for example, prolonging melatonin secretion by 30 minutes changes reproductive patterns.

Jet Lag Proves It

Scientists thought the extended melatonin dose was the answer to SAD—after all, as the days lengthen in spring, the melatonin-secretion phase shortens and humans revive their interest in life. But the explanation had a problem: there was no physiological evidence that an additional half an hour of melatonin caused depression. And pharmaceuticals that suppress synthesis of

the hormone did not seem to help SAD patients.

Researchers concluded that something more basic must be amiss in how SAD people sense light. Led by Alfred Lewy, head of the Sleep and Mood Disorders Laboratory at the Oregon Health & Science University, scientists in the past decade have devised a more comprehensive theory. In today's world, lit by incandescent, fluorescent and halogen lamps day and night, people have become more or less decoupled from the natural daylight cycle. In the morning, most people's inner clocks seem to register artificial light as weaker than sunlight, yet the rays are still enough of a sign to suppress melatonin secretion. Man-made light also keeps the expected production of melatonin at bay after the sun goes down. As a result, our circadian clocks tick somewhat independently of actual day length and season.

Not so for people with seasonal affective disorder. For SAD patients, the 100 to 500 lux brightness of typical homes is not enough to tell the SCN to halt the pineal gland. In the morning, the gland continues to secrete melatonin—at lower levels than at night but still to a greater degree than the normal near-zero of daytime. And in the

The longer daylight hours of spring cause SAD to suddenly disappear, and it stays away until autumn.

Melatonin Switch

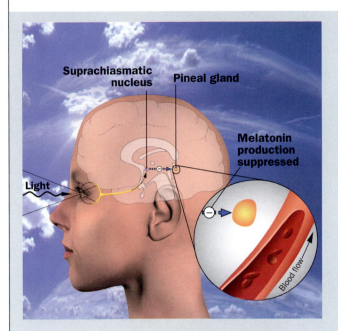

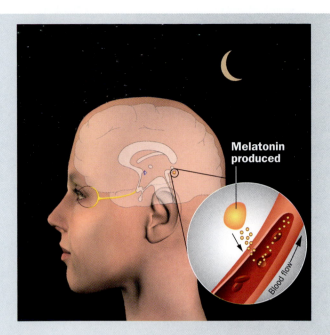

The passing of daylight hours is detected by the eye's retina and transmitted to the suprachiasmatic nucleus (SCN). This bundle of neurons, about the size of a grain of rice, lies in the hypothalamus, near the point where the two optic nerves cross, and operates as our master clock. It controls daily body rhythms, such as the activity of organs and the sleep-wake cycle. During daytime, the SCN fires powerfully and—through intermediate chemical steps—suppresses the secretion of melatonin, the "sleep hormone," by the pineal gland (*left*). At night the SCN firing drops, and melatonin flows into the bloodstream, making us drowsy (*right*).

evening melatonin rises despite the artificial lights, dampening mood by dinnertime and increasing the likelihood of depression.

Further refinement of this theory has pointed to a phase delay in melatonin secretion as the real culprit. The internal clocks of SAD patients not only go into night mode earlier in the evening and remain in night mode longer in the morning, they lag behind natural daylight time and trail other body rhythms. That our brains cannot readily shrug off such phase shifts is clear to anyone who has ever made a long-distance flight. Immediately after such a trip most people are not just tired but also grumpy and listless—jet lag has them down. After a few days their inner clocks adjust their phase to the new timing of dawn and dusk, and the symptoms disappear. David Avery of the University of Washington, who has studied seasonal depression for years, explains the analogy: "People with seasonal depression experience something like constant jet lag. They wake up and feel as if it is the middle of the night. And as several studies have shown, from a physiological point of view it really is the middle of the night for them."

Morning Shower of Light

Knowing the physical cause of SAD has lent credence—and specificity—to one form of therapy that has been gaining in recent years, according to anecdotal reports. In Hippocrates' day the remedy of choice was to have sufferers look at the sun, a practice that was somewhat hard on the eyes. Today so-called light boxes do a better job. The boxes, one or two feet on a side, contain special lamps that produce up to 10,000 lux of white light—equivalent to the outdoor light of a bright summer day.

For many patients, 30 to 45 minutes of bright light every day, begun during the dim stretches of autumn and continued throughout winter, improve their mind-sets demonstrably. The timing of the dose is important, however. According to various studies, soaking up the light at noon is worthless, and evening doses are of limited value for

(The Author)

ULRICH KRAFT is a physician and science writer in Berlin who in winter often flees the city for sunnier locales.

SIGANIM

improving patient moods. Early-morning applications are far and away the best. Patients must wake up early and sit directly in front of the boxes, typically while having coffee or looking at the day's newspaper. Apparently, the intensive light tells the timekeeping neurons in the suprachiasmatic nucleus that the day has begun, so it is time to end the nocturnal synthesis of melatonin. According to most reports, more than 60 percent of SAD patients respond to the morning showers of light.

Done every day, the regimen also appears to reset the clock so it is in proper phase again with the rest of the body. And that adjustment seems to correct the evening onset of melatonin secretion.

According to current treatment protocols, patients should be seated within one to two feet of the light boxes by 6 A.M. or so. Yet Michael Terman, a psychologist at Columbia University, says this strict regimen may have to be adjusted. "For some people, that time is much too early. What's important is not the time of day but the 'time' on each patient's circadian clock—where the person is in his or her daily cycle of melatonin production." By taking blood samples to determine melatonin levels, Terman has found the most effective timing of light treatment for dozens of patients. They seem to benefit most when they sit in front of the lamps about eight hours after their bodies start producing the hormone the evening before.

More Serotonin, Please

More recently, one of the brain's chemical messengers has been implicated as a co-conspirator in the wintertime blues: serotonin. This neurotransmitter affects various aspects of appetite, sleep and, most important, mood. Serotonin plays a decisive role in many types of depression, and increasingly, depressed patients are being treated with drugs that delay the reuptake of serotonin, keeping levels in the blood higher. It turns out that these so-called SSRIs—selective serotonin reuptake inhibitors—also help people with seasonal mood swings.

This correlation suggests that as autumn daylight diminishes, the serotonin levels in SAD sufferers change inappropriately. Various studies have since revealed that most people's serotonin levels reach an annual low point during January and rise with the longer days of spring. But new thinking suggests that falling serotonin levels could conspire to make certain individuals depressed if they have one kind of genetic makeup.

Just like every other gene in our bodies, two copies of the so-called *5-HTTLPR* gene exist in-

SAD sufferers can brighten their mood by sitting early each morning directly in front of special light boxes that simulate strong natural sunlight.

NAILAH FEANNY Corbis

From Bulimia to Jet Lag

Light therapy has succeeded in fending off seasonal affective disorder—and with virtually no side effects. Though not a miracle cure, it is helping people overcome other challenging conditions:

Bulimia. This binge-eating disorder, which primarily afflicts young women, is associated with serious psychological maladies. But psychologist Raymond Lam of the University of British Columbia in Vancouver realized that many of his patients fared worse in January than in June. He has conducted studies in which he has bulimic women sit in front of light boxes every day, and after only a couple of sessions both their psychological and eating difficulties seemed to ease.

Sleep delay. Some people cannot fall asleep until very late at night and often cannot get moving again until 10 or 11 A.M. The reason: their internal clocks are out of phase with the natural day-night cycle. In some cases, extended bouts can inexplicably reverse: sufferers crash by early evening and end up waking hours before dawn. Scott Campbell, a chronobiologist at New York Presbyterian Hospital/Weill Cornell Medical Center, has had some success correcting this phase problem; people who fall asleep too late are exposed to light in the early morn-

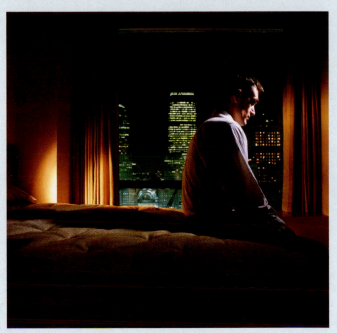

ing, whereas the early risers will get the light at night.

Shift workers. One week they work 8 A.M. to 4 P.M.; the next week their schedule is from midnight to eight in the morning. Almost no shift worker escapes the consequences of this circadian whiplash. At a minimum, many become fatigued and have trouble concentrating when working nights. Although their inner clocks can adjust, the transition takes several days, and then almost immediately they must switch back. Researchers have found that shift workers make the transition much more easily when the workplace is bathed in at least 1,200 lux of light—what would be found in a bright office. Often, however, occupational safety laws require only 500 lux or so.

Jet lag. After a trip across many time zones, an individual's circadian clock usually needs several days to reset. The most obvious symptoms are sleep problems. Researchers disagree about whether light therapy can speed the reset process, but doctors nonetheless urge long-distance travelers to get as much daylight or bright light as possible during the first few days. Some hotels now offer in-room light boxes or special lamps that simulate sunrise to help the jet-lagged adjust. —*U.K.*

---

side every cell. But the two "alleles" are not necessarily identical; there is a short version and a long version. In 1998 a research group led by Rosenthal at the NIMH found that people with at least one short allele are more prone to seasonal depression and to more severe symptoms. Multiple studies have found a hereditary pattern, too; in the families of SAD patients, 13 to 17 percent of immediate relatives also suffer from seasonal depression. In the general population, the rate varies from 1.4 to 9.7 percent depending on the distance from the equator.

Genes, changes in levels of important hormones and neurotransmitters, an out-of-sync circadian clock—many factors seem to play a role in seasonal depression. But this disorder makes one thing clear: even in the 21st century, human

beings are not independent of nature. Our inner clocks still track the seasons. For all we know, evolution may favor sluggishness in fall and winter as a way to promote physical and psychological renewal. Perhaps the problem is that in today's world such a life in tune with the seasons is no longer possible, and the SAD individuals are trying harder to preserve human nature. **M**

(Further Reading)

◆ **Winter Blues: Seasonal Affective Disorder: What It Is and How to Overcome It.** Norman E. Rosenthal. Guilford Press, 1998.
◆ **Pathophysiology of Seasonal Affective Disorder: A Review.** Raymond W. Lam and Robert D. Levitan in *Journal of Psychiatry Neuroscience*, Vol. 25, pages 469–480; 2000.
◆ **Positive Options for Seasonal Affective Disorder (SAD): Self-Help and Treatment.** Fiona Marshall and Peter Cheevers. Hunter House, 2003.

Frequent washing is a ritual shared by a number of people who have obsessive-compulsive disorder.

Taming

Compulsion

For people trapped in obsessive-compulsive thoughts and rituals, therapy and medication may offer the best way out

BY MARION SONNENMOSER

Even as a girl, Ursula had a penchant for tidiness. Her parents encouraged her tendencies, reminding her not to get dirty. As a young woman, her disdain for germs became an unhealthy preoccupation. She would not let visitors into her home for fear they might bring in dirt or bacteria. Panicked by the idea of infection, she declined invitations to family outings and wore gloves, even in midsummer. She cleaned her house thoroughly several times a day. Even when everything appeared spotless, the young woman avoided handling any of the doorknobs in her house. If she did happen to touch one, she immediately scrubbed the offending finger with disinfectant until it was red and raw. Ursula (her last name withheld to protect privacy) knew her behavior was excessive, but she could not stop.

Ursula is among the approximately 2 percent of all people who suffer from obsessive-compulsive disorder, or OCD. This disorder may take many forms. Some patients' rituals involve washing or checking again and again to see if a burner or faucet has been turned off. Other patients are plagued by thoughts that frequently revolve around religion, sex or physical aggression. They often live in fear that their fantasies could turn into unwanted reality and struggle desperately against their repetitive behaviors. "There is no way to outwit the compulsion," wrote Ursula in her diary.

FAST FACTS
Obsessive-Compulsive Disorder

1 >> Obsessive-compulsive disorder (OCD) involves involuntary, repetitive thoughts—ideas, impulses, images—or repeated stereotyped behaviors, which generally serve to diffuse fear and tension in the patient.

2 >> Two percent of all people suffer from OCD—six million in the U.S. alone.

3 >> Recent research shows that psychological and biological factors play a role in the onset of OCD, so successful treatment most often requires a combination of psychotherapy and medicines.

"There is no way to outwit the compulsion," wrote Ursula in her diary. Untreated, the habits may grow more elaborate over time.

OCD is thought to result from overarousal of the feedback loop controlling behavior, located in the frontal cortex, basal ganglion and thalamus.

(Out of Balance)

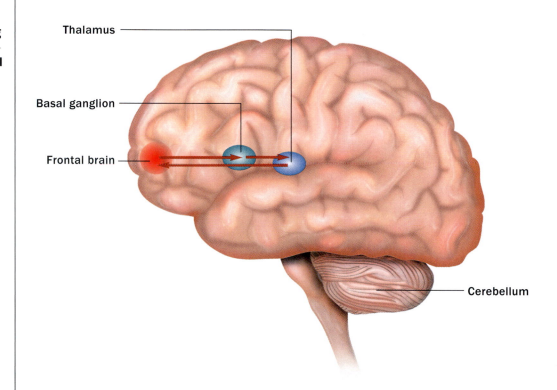

- Thalamus
- Basal ganglion
- Frontal brain
- Cerebellum

Untreated, the habits may grow more elaborate over time.

Foundations of Obsession

No single root cause has been found for OCD, although it seems to involve both psychological and physical factors. A decisive or unpleasant event may trigger the disorder. For Ursula, it was entry into her professional career: she felt overwhelmed and was plunged into self-doubt. Eventually she experienced an outbreak—"explosive," she wrote—of compulsive behavior.

OCD seems to run in families, suggesting it has a genetic component, although no specific gene has been identified. "The influence of genetics, however, seems to be less in obsessive-compulsive disorders than in other mental problems," says Wolfgang Maier, who studies the genetics of psychiatric ailments at the University of Bonn in Germany.

Injuries or infections in particular regions of the brain can also lead to OCD. These areas are typically the basal ganglion, the frontal brain and the thalamus, which are bound into a feedback loop that collectively controls our behavior [see illustration above]. In OCD, this control system gets out of balance. The caudate nucleus (one of the masses of nerve cells within the basal ganglion) and the frontal brain work with extraordinary intensity. That unusual activity is difficult for the brain to shut off. After deciding to do something, people with OCD have trouble responding to new outside stimuli or events. "They get trapped in a motor or cognitive process once they start," explains Fritz Hohagen, director of the Lübeck University Clinic for Psychiatry and Psychotherapy, which specializes in caring for OCD patients.

(The Author)

MARION SONNENMOSER has a degree in psychology and is a science writer in the Palatinate region of Germany.

SIGANIM *Gehirn & Geist*

Two-Pronged Treatment

With both mental and physical factors at work in OCD, successful remedies generally combine behavioral and medical approaches. Behavioral therapy can help the patient, step by step, do what she once feared so much, such as touching a "contaminated" handrail.

At the outset of therapy, "assessment of thoughts plays an important role in successful treatment of obsessive-compulsive disorders," explains Hans Reinecker, professor of clinical psychology at the University of Bamberg in Germany. Ursula, for example, could not bear it when she saw someone spit on the street. She was not just annoyed and disgusted—she actually felt threatened. A healthy person might have experienced brief revulsion and then moved on. But the young woman could not shake her thoughts of filth and germs. Her inner tensions grew until they were released by an episode of hand washing. Afterward she felt better, but only briefly; her thoughts soon circled back to the filth.

Compulsive behaviors are often just the outlet for tormenting thoughts. In their conversations, therapists and patients must therefore discuss such extreme feelings and obsessions. The patient learns to withstand uncertainty and inner tension, to reflect on her behavior and to accept imperfection. The heart of the therapy lies in confrontation: the therapist leads the patient to face first imaginary, then real, objects of her fear. Ursula, for example, had to climb an observation tower, which meant grabbing the banisters repeatedly. She agreed to try it without wearing gloves or washing her hands. Performing this exercise and many others taught Ursula that her fears about infection were unfounded. Gradually, she developed a more relaxed attitude toward dirt.

Calming the Feedback Loop

Drugs called serotonin reuptake inhibitors, a class that includes some antidepressants, also can moderate symptoms of OCD. Serotonin is a neurotransmitter, a chemical messenger in the brain. Scientists believe that in OCD patients the sensitivity of the serotonin receptors decreases. This change could, in turn, cause overarousal of the feedback loop that normally helps to control behavior, because many nerve cells that use serotonin as a messenger substance terminate in the thalamus, basal ganglion or frontal brain.

When therapy and drugs fail, surgery may be the next step. The operations involve the thermal destruction of areas in a brain region called the gyrus cinguli or the severing of fibers linking the

OCD sufferers are often aware that behaviors such as repeated house cleanings are excessive but feel they cannot stop.

frontal brain and caudate nucleus. Using a "brain pacemaker," also known as deep-brain stimulation, is still an experimental approach to OCD. (At present, the Food and Drug Administration has approved the technique only for certain ailments, and OCD is not yet one of them.) A surgeon inserts small electrodes into the lower part of the forebrain through holes bored into a patient's skull. A pacemaker implanted below the skin of the chest sends weak electrical impulses through the electrodes intended to moderate the processes that lead to the patient's uncontrollable repeated behaviors. Brain surgeon Volker Sturm of the department of stereotactic and functional neurosurgery at Cologne University in Germany has implanted such pacemakers in five patients since 1999. Three of them now are apparently symptom-free. In the fourth patient, a technical problem (dislocation of the electrode) prevented the pacemaker from having any effect. The other patient, who was also schizophrenic, discontinued treatment during testing because of paranoid thoughts.

Ursula, after two years of behavioral therapy, has conquered OCD without such measures. She can now make plans to go out with friends and family, have visitors over and enjoy experiences she did without for so long. In fact, she recently confided to her therapist that she has a new problem: smile lines.

(Further Reading)

◆ **Tormenting Thoughts and Secret Rituals: The Hidden Epidemic of Obsessive-Compulsive Disorder.** Ian Osborn. Dell Publishing Company, 1999.
◆ **Getting Control: Overcoming Your Obsessions and Compulsions.** Lee Baer. Plume Books, 2000.
◆ The Obsessive-Compulsion Foundation's Web site is available at **www.ocfoundation.org/**

Drug abuse produces
long-term changes in the
reward circuitry of the brain.
Knowledge of the cellular
and molecular details of these
adaptations could lead to new
treatments for the compulsive
behaviors that underlie addiction

The Addicted BRAIN

By Eric J. Nestler and Robert C. Malenka

ILLUSTRATION BY JANA BRENNING (photograph used for illustration purposes only)

White lines on a mirror. A needle and spoon. For many users, the sight of a drug or its associated paraphernalia can elicit shudders of anticipatory pleasure. Then, with the fix, comes the real rush: the warmth, the clarity, the vision, the relief, the sensation of being at the center of the universe. For a brief period, everything feels right. But something happens after repeated exposure to drugs of abuse—whether heroin or cocaine, whiskey or speed.

The amount that once produced euphoria doesn't work as well, and users come to need a shot or a snort just to feel normal; without it, they become depressed and, often, physically ill. Then they begin to use the drug compulsively. At this point, they are addicted, losing control over their use and suffering powerful cravings even after the thrill is gone and their habit begins to harm their health, finances and personal relationships.

Neurobiologists have long known that the euphoria induced by drugs of abuse arises because all these chemicals ultimately boost the activity of the brain's reward system:

ADDICTION ARISES in part because habit-forming drugs cause the brain's circuit for assessing reward to deem the drugs more desirable than anything else in life.

a complex circuit of nerve cells, or neurons, that evolved to make us feel flush after eating or sex—things we need to do to survive and pass along our genes. At least initially, goosing this system makes us feel good and encourages us to repeat whatever activity brought us such pleasure.

But new research indicates that chronic drug use induces changes in the structure and function of the system's neurons that last for weeks, months or years after the last fix. These adaptations, perversely, dampen the pleasurable effects of a chronically abused substance yet also increase the cravings that trap the addict in a destructive spiral of escalating use and increased fallout at work and at home. Improved understanding of these neural alterations should help provide better interventions for addiction, so that people who have fallen prey to habit-forming drugs can reclaim their brains and their lives.

Drugs to Die For

THE REALIZATION that various drugs of abuse ultimately lead to addiction through a common pathway emerged largely from studies of laboratory animals that began about 40 years ago. Given the opportunity, rats, mice and nonhuman primates will self-administer the same substances that humans abuse. In these experiments, the animals are connected to an intravenous line. They are then taught to press one lever to receive an infusion of drug through the IV, another lever to get a relatively uninteresting saline solution, and a third lever to request a food pellet. Within a few days, the animals are hooked: they readily self-administer cocaine, heroin, amphetamine and

THE BRAIN UNDER THE INFLUENCE

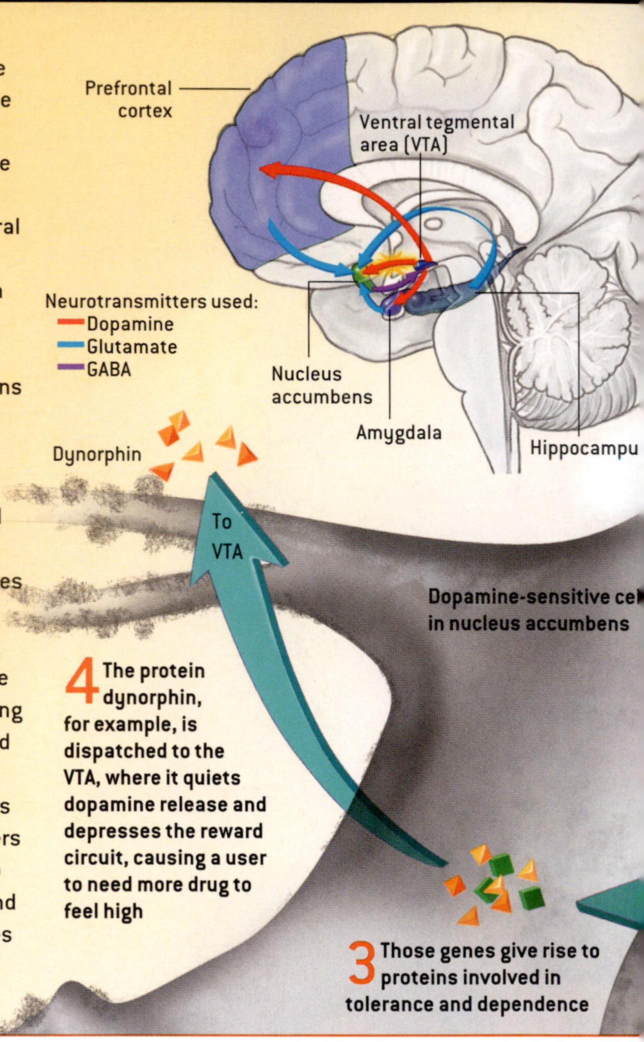

CHRONIC USE of addictive substances can change the behavior of a key part of the brain's reward circuit: the pathway extending from the dopamine-producing nerve cells (neurons) of the ventral tegmental area (VTA) to dopamine-sensitive cells in the nucleus accumbens. Those changes, induced in part by the molecular actions depicted at the right and in the graph, contribute significantly to the tolerance, dependence and craving that fuel repeated drug use and lead to relapses even after long periods of abstention. The colored arrows on the brain indicate some of the pathways linking the nucleus accumbens and VTA with other regions that can help to make drug users highly sensitive to reminders of past highs, vulnerable to relapses when stressed, and unable to control their urges to seek drugs.

Prefrontal cortex

Ventral tegmental area (VTA)

Neurotransmitters used:
- Dopamine
- Glutamate
- GABA

Nucleus accumbens

Amygdala

Hippocampus

Dynorphin

To VTA

Dopamine-sensitive cells in nucleus accumbens

4 The protein dynorphin, for example, is dispatched to the VTA, where it quiets dopamine release and depresses the reward circuit, causing a user to need more drug to feel high

3 Those genes give rise to proteins involved in tolerance and dependence

many other common habit-forming drugs.

What is more, they eventually display assorted behaviors of addiction. Individual animals will take drugs at the expense of normal activities such as eating and sleeping—some even to the point that they die of exhaustion or malnutrition. For the

most addictive substances, such as cocaine, animals will spend most of their waking hours working to obtain more, even if it means pressing a lever hundreds of times for a single hit. And just as human addicts experience intense cravings when they encounter drug paraphernalia or places where they have scored, the animals, too, come to prefer an environment that they associate with the drug—an area in the cage in which lever pressing always provides chemical compensation.

When the substance is taken away, the animals soon cease to labor for chemical satisfaction. But the pleasure is not forgotten. A rat that has remained clean—even for months—will immediately return to its bar-pressing behavior when given just a taste of cocaine or placed in a cage it associates with a drug high. And certain

Overview/*The Evolution of Addiction*

- Drugs of abuse—cocaine, alcohol, opiates, amphetamine—all commandeer the brain's natural reward circuitry. Stimulation of this pathway reinforces behaviors, ensuring that whatever you just did, you'll want to do again.
- Repeated exposure to these drugs induces long-lasting adaptations in the brain's chemistry and architecture, altering how individual neurons in the brain's reward pathways process information and interact with one another.
- Understanding how chronic exposure to drugs of abuse reshapes an addict's brain could lead to novel, more broadly effective ways to correct the cellular and molecular aberrations that lie at the heart of all addiction.

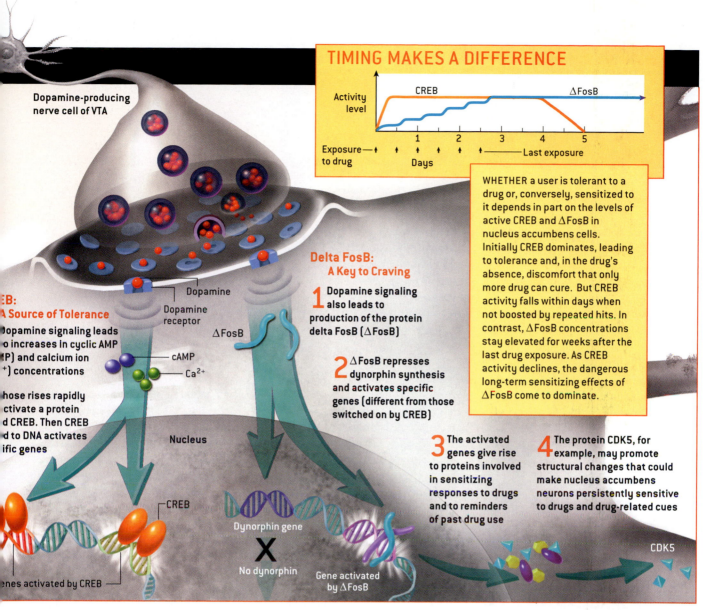

TIMING MAKES A DIFFERENCE

Activity level

CREB   ΔFosB

Exposure to drug
1   2   3   4   5
Days   Last exposure

WHETHER a user is tolerant to a drug or, conversely, sensitized to it depends in part on the levels of active CREB and ΔFosB in nucleus accumbens cells. Initially CREB dominates, leading to tolerance and, in the drug's absence, discomfort that only more drug can cure. But CREB activity falls within days when not boosted by repeated hits. In contrast, ΔFosB concentrations stay elevated for weeks after the last drug exposure. As CREB activity declines, the dangerous long-term sensitizing effects of ΔFosB come to dominate.

Dopamine-producing nerve cell of VTA

Dopamine

Dopamine receptor

ΔFosB

Delta FosB: A Key to Craving

1 Dopamine signaling also leads to production of the protein delta FosB (ΔFosB)

2 ΔFosB represses dynorphin synthesis and activates specific genes (different from those switched on by CREB)

3 The activated genes give rise to proteins involved in sensitizing responses to drugs and to reminders of past drug use

4 The protein CDK5, for example, may promote structural changes that could make nucleus accumbens neurons persistently sensitive to drugs and drug-related cues

EB: A Source of Tolerance

Dopamine signaling leads to increases in cyclic AMP (AMP) and calcium ion (+) concentrations

hose rises rapidly activate a protein d CREB. Then CREB d to DNA activates ific genes

cAMP

Ca^{2+}

Nucleus

CREB

Dynorphin gene

X

No dynorphin

Gene activated by ΔFosB

enes activated by CREB

CDK5

---

psychological stresses, such as a periodic, unexpected foot shock, will send rats scurrying back to drugs. These same types of stimuli—exposure to low doses of drug, drug-associated cues or stress—trigger craving and relapse in human addicts.

Using this self-administration setup and related techniques, researchers mapped the regions of the brain that mediate addictive behaviors and discovered the central role of the brain's reward circuit. Drugs commandeer this circuit, stimulating its activity with a force and persistence greater than any natural reward.

A key component of the reward circuitry is the mesolimbic dopamine system: a set of nerve cells that originate in the ventral tegmental area (VTA), near the base of the brain, and send projections to target regions in the front of the brain—

most notably to a structure deep beneath the frontal cortex called the nucleus accumbens. Those VTA neurons communicate by dispatching the chemical messenger (neurotransmitter) dopamine from the terminals, or tips, of their long projections to receptors on nucleus accumbens neurons. The dopamine pathway from the VTA to the nucleus accumbens is critical for addiction: animals with lesions in these brain regions no longer show interest in substances of abuse.

Rheostat of Reward

REWARD PATHWAYS are evolutionarily ancient. Even the simple, soil-dwelling worm *Caenorhabditis elegans* possesses a rudimentary version. In these worms, inactivation of four to eight key dopamine-containing neurons causes an ani-

mal to plow straight past a heap of bacteria, its favorite meal.

In mammals, the reward circuit is more complex, and it is integrated with several other brain regions that serve to color an experience with emotion and direct the individual's response to rewarding stimuli, including food, sex and social interaction. The amygdala, for instance, helps to assess whether an experience is pleasurable or aversive—and whether it should be repeated or avoided—and helps to forge connections between an experience and other cues; the hippocampus participates in recording the memories of an experience, including where and when and with whom it occurred; and the frontal regions of the cerebral cortex coordinate and process all this information and determine the ultimate behavior of the

INSIGHTS FROM IMAGING

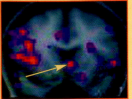

Nucleus accumbens

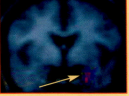

Amygdala

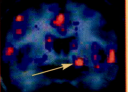

Sublenticular extended amygdala

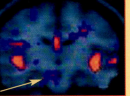

Ventral tegmental area

Prefrontal cortex

SPOTS OF COLOR in brain scans of cocaine addicts (*above*) confirm animal studies indicating that drug intake can induce profound immediate activity changes in many brain regions, including those shown; brightest spots show the most significant change. While being scanned, the subjects rated their feelings of rush and craving on a scale of zero to three—revealing that the VTA and the sublenticular extended amygdala are important to the cocaine-induced rush and that the amygdala and the nucleus accumbens influence both the rush and the craving for more drug, which becomes stronger as the euphoria wears off (*graph*).

individual. The VTA-accumbens pathway, meanwhile, acts as a rheostat of reward: it "tells" the other brain centers how rewarding an activity is. The more rewarding an activity is deemed, the more likely the organism is to remember it well and repeat it.

Although most knowledge of the brain's reward circuitry has been derived from animals, brain-imaging studies conducted over the past 10 years have revealed that equivalent pathways control natural and drug rewards in humans. Using functional magnetic resonance imaging (fMRI) or positron emission tomography (PET) scans (techniques that measure changes in blood flow associated with neuronal activity), researchers have watched the nucleus accumbens in cocaine addicts light up when they are offered a snort. When the same addicts are shown a video of someone using cocaine or a photograph of white lines on a mirror, the accumbens responds similarly, along with the amygdala and some areas of the cortex. And the same regions react in compulsive gamblers who are shown images of slot machines, suggesting that the VTA-accumbens pathway has a similarly critical role even in nondrug addictions.

Dopamine, Please

HOW IS IT POSSIBLE that diverse addictive substances—which have no common structural features and exert a variety of effects on the body—all elicit similar responses in the brain's reward circuitry? How can cocaine, a stimulant that causes the heart to race, and heroin, a pain-relieving sedative, be so opposite in some ways and yet alike in targeting the reward system? The answer is that all drugs of abuse, in addition to any other effects, cause the nucleus accumbens to receive a flood of dopamine and sometimes also dopamine-mimicking signals.

When a nerve cell in the VTA is excited, it sends an electrical message racing along its axon—the signal-carrying "highway" that extends into the nucleus accumbens. The signal causes dopamine to be released from the axon tip into the tiny space—the synaptic cleft—that separates the axon terminal from a neuron in the nucleus accumbens. From there, the dopamine latches onto its receptor on the accumbens neuron and transmits its signal into the cell. To later shut down the signal, the VTA neuron removes the dopamine from the synaptic cleft and repackages it to be used again as needed.

Cocaine and other stimulants temporarily disable the transporter protein that returns the neurotransmitter to the VTA neuron terminals, thereby leaving excess dopamine to act on the nucleus accumbens. Heroin and other opiates, on the other hand, bind to neurons in the VTA that normally shut down the dopamine-producing VTA neurons. The opi-

ates release this cellular clamp, thus freeing the dopamine-secreting cells to pour extra dopamine into the nucleus accumbens. Opiates can also generate a strong "reward" message by acting directly on the nucleus accumbens.

But drugs do more than provide the dopamine jolt that induces euphoria and mediates the initial reward and reinforcement. Over time and with repeated exposure, they initiate the gradual adaptations in the reward circuitry that give rise to addiction.

An Addiction Is Born

THE EARLY STAGES of addiction are characterized by tolerance and dependence. After a drug binge, an addict needs more of the substance to get the same effect on mood or concentration and so on. This tolerance then provokes an escalation of drug use that engenders dependence—a need that manifests itself as painful emotional and, at times, physical reactions if access to a drug is cut off. Both tolerance and dependence occur because frequent drug use can, ironically, suppress parts of the brain's reward circuit.

At the heart of this cruel suppression lies a molecule known as CREB (cAMP response element-binding protein). CREB is a transcription factor, a protein that regulates the expression, or activity, of genes and thus the overall behavior of

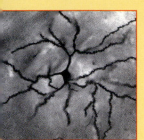

MICROGRAPHS of nucleus accumbens neurons in animals exposed to nonaddictive drugs display dendritic branches with normal numbers of signal-receiving projections called spines (*left* and *center*). But those who become addicted to cocaine sprout additional spines on the branches, which consequently look bushier (*right*). Presumably, such remodeling makes neurons more sensitive to signals from the VTA and elsewhere and thus contributes to drug sensitivity. Recent findings suggest that delta FosB plays a part in spine growth.

nerve cells. When drugs of abuse are administered, dopamine concentrations in the nucleus accumbens rise, inducing dopamine-responsive cells to increase production of a small signaling molecule, cyclic AMP (cAMP), which in turn activates CREB. After CREB is switched on, it binds to a specific set of genes, triggering production of the proteins those genes encode.

Chronic drug use causes sustained activation of CREB, which enhances expression of its target genes, some of which code for proteins that then dampen the reward circuitry. For example, CREB controls the production of dynorphin, a natural molecule with opiumlike effects. Dynorphin is synthesized by a subset of neurons in the nucleus accumbens that loop back and inhibit neurons in the VTA. Induction of dynorphin by CREB thereby stifles the brain's reward circuitry, inducing tolerance by making the same-old dose of drug less rewarding. The increase in dynorphin also contributes to dependence, as its inhibition of the reward pathway leaves the individual, in the drug's absence, depressed and unable to take pleasure in previously enjoyable activities.

But CREB is only a piece of the story. This transcription factor is switched off within days after drug use stops. So CREB cannot account for the longer-lasting grip that abused substances have on

the brain—for the brain alterations that cause addicts to return to a substance even after years or decades of abstinence. Such relapse is driven to a large extent by sensitization, a phenomenon whereby the effects of a drug are augmented.

Although it might sound counterintuitive, the same drug can evoke both tolerance and sensitization. Shortly after a hit, CREB activity is high and tolerance rules: for several days, the user would need increasing amounts of drug to goose the reward circuit. But if the addict abstains, CREB activity declines. At that point, tolerance wanes and sensitization sets in, kicking off the intense craving that underlies the compulsive drug-seeking behavior of addiction. A mere taste or a memory can draw the addict back. This relentless yearning persists even after long periods of abstention. To understand the roots of sensitization, we have to look for molecular changes that last longer than a few days. One candidate culprit is another transcription factor: delta FosB.

Road to Relapse

DELTA FOSB APPEARS to function very differently in addiction than CREB does. Studies of mice and rats indicate that in response to chronic drug abuse, delta FosB concentrations rise gradually and progressively in the nucleus accumbens and other brain regions. Moreover, because the protein is extraordinarily stable, it remains active in these nerve cells for weeks to months after drug administration, a persistence that would enable it to maintain changes in gene expression long after drug taking ceased.

Studies of mutant mice that produce excessive amounts of delta FosB in the nucleus accumbens show that prolonged induction of this molecule causes animals to become hypersensitive to drugs. These mice were highly prone to relapse after the drugs were withdrawn and later made available—a finding implying that delta FosB concentrations could well contribute to long-term increases in sensitivity in the reward pathways of humans. Interestingly, delta FosB is also produced in the nucleus accumbens in mice in response to repetitious nondrug rewards, such as excessive wheel running and sugar consumption. Hence, it might have a more general role in the development of compulsive behavior toward a wide range of rewarding stimuli.

Recent evidence hints at a mechanism for how sensitization could persist even after delta FosB concentrations return to normal. Chronic exposure to cocaine and other drugs of abuse is known to induce the signal-receiving branches of nucleus accumbens neurons to sprout additional buds, termed dendritic spines, that bolster the cells' connections to other neurons. In rodents, this sprouting can continue for some months after drug taking ceases. This discovery suggests that delta FosB may be responsible for the added

THE AUTHORS

ERIC J. NESTLER and ROBERT C. MALENKA study the molecular basis of drug addiction. Nestler, professor in and chair of the department of psychiatry at the University of Texas Southwestern Medical Center at Dallas, was elected to the Institute of Medicine in 1998. Malenka, professor of psychiatry and behavioral sciences at the Stanford University School of Medicine, joined the faculty there after serving as director of the Center for the Neurobiology of Addiction at the University of California, San Francisco. With Steven E. Hyman, now at Harvard University, Nestler and Malenka wrote the textbook *Molecular Basis of Neuropharmacology* (McGraw-Hill, 2001).

DIFFERENT DRUGS, SAME ULTIMATE EFFECT

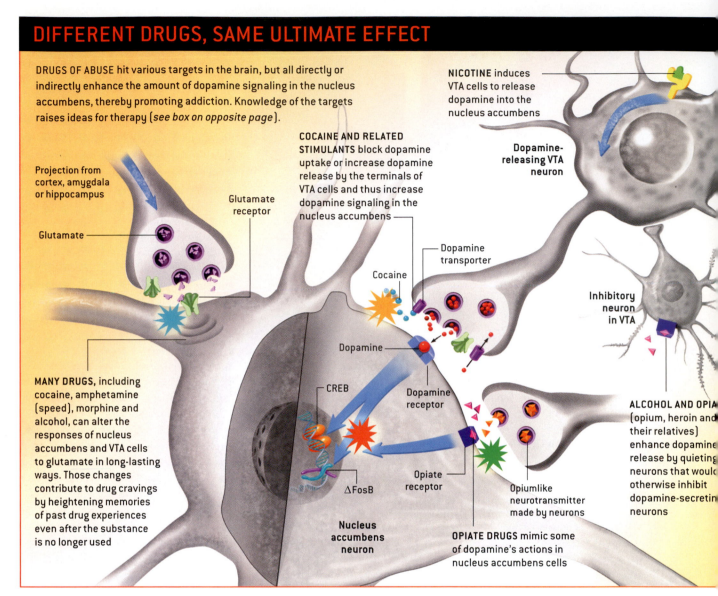

DRUGS OF ABUSE hit various targets in the brain, but all directly or indirectly enhance the amount of dopamine signaling in the nucleus accumbens, thereby promoting addiction. Knowledge of the targets raises ideas for therapy (*see box on opposite page*).

NICOTINE induces VTA cells to release dopamine into the nucleus accumbens

COCAINE AND RELATED STIMULANTS block dopamine uptake or increase dopamine release by the terminals of VTA cells and thus increase dopamine signaling in the nucleus accumbens

Projection from cortex, amygdala or hippocampus

Glutamate

Glutamate receptor

Dopamine-releasing VTA neuron

Dopamine transporter

Cocaine

Inhibitory neuron in VTA

Dopamine

CREB

Dopamine receptor

MANY DRUGS, including cocaine, amphetamine (speed), morphine and alcohol, can alter the responses of nucleus accumbens and VTA cells to glutamate in long-lasting ways. Those changes contribute to drug cravings by heightening memories of past drug experiences even after the substance is no longer used

ΔFosB

Opiate receptor

Nucleus accumbens neuron

Opiumlike neurotransmitter made by neurons

OPIATE DRUGS mimic some of dopamine's actions in nucleus accumbens cells

ALCOHOL AND OPIA (opium, heroin and their relatives) enhance dopamine release by quieting neurons that would otherwise inhibit dopamine-secretin neurons

---

spines. Highly speculative extrapolation from these results raises the possibility that the extra connections generated by delta FosB activity amplify signaling between the linked cells for years and that such heightened signaling might cause the brain to overreact to drug-related cues. The dendritic changes may, in the end, be the key adaptation that accounts for the intransigence of addiction.

Learning Addiction

THUS FAR WE HAVE focused on drug-induced changes that relate to dopamine in the brain's reward system. Recall, however, that other brain regions—namely, the amygdala, hippocampus and frontal cortex—are involved in addiction and communicate back and forth with the VTA and the nucleus accumbens. All those regions talk to the reward pathway by releasing the neurotransmitter glutamate. When drugs of abuse increase dopamine release from the VTA into the nucleus accumbens, they also alter the responsiveness of the VTA and nucleus accumbens to glutamate for days. Animal experiments indicate that changes in sensitivity to glutamate in the reward pathway enhance both the release of dopamine from the VTA and responsiveness to dopamine in the nucleus accumbens, thereby promoting CREB and delta FosB activity and the unhappy effects of these molecules. Furthermore, it seems that this altered glutamate sensitivity strengthens the neuronal pathways that link memories of drug-taking experiences with high reward, thereby feeding the desire to seek the drug.

The mechanism by which drugs alter sensitivity to glutamate in neurons of the reward pathway is not yet known with certainty, but a working hypothesis can be formulated based on how glutamate affects neurons in the hippocampus. There certain types of short-term stimuli can enhance a cell's response to glutamate over many hours. The phenomenon, dubbed long-term potentiation, helps memories to form and appears to be mediated by the shuttling of certain glutamate-binding receptor proteins from intracellular stores, where they are not functional, to the nerve cell membrane, where they can respond to glutamate released into a synapse. Drugs of abuse influence the shuttling of glutamate receptors in the

TREATMENT POSSIBILITIES

Hypothetical anticocaine agent might reduce dopamine signaling in the nucleus accumbens by interfering with cocaine's ability to block dopamine uptake by VTA neuron terminals.

Hypothetical broad-spectrum agent would mute dopamine's effects by preventing CREB or ΔFosB from accumulating or from activating the target genes of these molecules.

Hypothetical broad-spectrum agent might interfere with the unhelpful changes in glutamate signaling that occur in nucleus accumbens cells with chronic drug use.

Opiate antagonists (such as naltrexone), already on the market, block opiate receptors. They are used against alcoholism and cigarette smoking because alcohol and nicotine trigger release of the brain's own opiumlike molecules.

reward pathway. Some findings suggest that they can also influence the synthesis of certain glutamate receptors.

Taken together, all the drug-induced changes in the reward circuit that we have discussed ultimately promote tolerance, dependence, craving, relapse and the complicated behaviors that accompany addiction. Many details remain mysterious, but we can say some things with assurance. During prolonged drug use, and shortly after use ceases, changes in the concentrations of cyclic AMP and the activity of CREB in neurons in the reward pathway predominate. These alterations cause tolerance and dependence, reducing sensitivity to the drug and rendering the addict depressed and lacking motivation. With more prolonged abstention, changes

in delta FosB activity and glutamate signaling predominate. These actions seem to be the ones that draw an addict back for more—by increasing sensitivity to the drug's effects if it is used again after a lapse and by eliciting powerful responses to memories of past highs and to cues that bring those memories to mind.

The revisions in CREB, delta FosB and glutamate signaling are central to addiction, but they certainly are not the whole story. As research progresses, neuroscientists will surely uncover other important molecular and cellular adaptations in the reward circuit and in related brain areas that will illuminate the true nature of addiction.

A Common Cure?

BEYOND IMPROVING understanding of the biological basis of drug addiction, the discovery of these molecular alterations provides novel targets for the biochemical treatment of this disorder. And the need for fresh therapies is enormous. In addition to addiction's obvious physical and psychological damage, the condition is a leading cause of medical illness. Alcoholics are prone to cirrhosis of the liver, smokers are susceptible to lung cancer, and heroin addicts spread HIV when they share needles. Addiction's toll on health and productivity in the U.S. has been estimated at more than $300 billion a year, making it one of the most serious problems facing society. If the definition of addiction is broadened to encompass other forms of compulsive pathological behavior, such as overeating and gambling, the costs are far higher. Therapies that could correct aberrant, addictive reactions to rewarding stimuli—whether cocaine or cheesecake or the thrill of winning at blackjack—would provide an enormous benefit to society.

Today's treatments fail to cure most addicts. Some medications prevent the

drug from getting to its target. These measures leave users with an "addicted brain" and intense drug craving. Other medical interventions mimic a drug's effects and thereby dampen craving long enough for an addict to kick the habit. These chemical substitutes, however, may merely replace one habit with another. And although nonmedical, rehabilitative treatments—such as the popular 12-step programs—help many people grapple with their addictions, participants still relapse at a high rate.

Armed with insight into the biology of addiction, researchers may one day be able to design medicines that counter or compensate for the long-term effects of drugs of abuse on reward regions in the brain. Compounds that interact specifically with the receptors that bind to glutamate or dopamine in the nucleus accumbens, or chemicals that prevent CREB or delta FosB from acting on their target genes in that area, could potentially loosen a drug's grip on an addict.

Furthermore, we need to learn to recognize those individuals who are most prone to addiction. Although psychological, social and environmental factors certainly are important, studies in susceptible families suggest that in humans about 50 percent of the risk for drug addiction is genetic. The particular genes involved have not yet been identified, but if susceptible individuals could be recognized early on, interventions could be targeted to this vulnerable population.

Because emotional and social factors operate in addiction, we cannot expect medications to fully treat the syndrome of addiction. But we can hope that future therapies will dampen the intense biological forces—the dependence, the cravings—that drive addiction and will thereby make psychosocial interventions more effective in helping to rebuild an addict's body and mind. SA

MORE TO EXPLORE

Incentive-Sensitization and Addiction. Terry E. Robinson and Kent C. Berridge in *Addiction,* Vol. 96, No. 1, pages 103–114; January 2001.

Molecular Basis of Long-Term Plasticity underlying Addiction. Eric J. Nestler in *Nature Reviews Neuroscience,* Vol. 2, No. 2, pages 119–128; February 2001.

Addiction: From Biology to Drug Policy. Second edition. A. Goldstein. Oxford University Press, 2001.

National Institute on Drug Abuse Information on Common Drugs of Abuse: **www.nida.nih.gov/DrugPages/**

HEAD ATTACK

You're late, the traffic is a nightmare and you're yelling at the kids to stop fighting in the back. Is your mental stress putting you at greater risk for a heart attack?

By Michael Feld and Johann Caspar Rüegg

G erry suddenly clutched at his chest. His heart was racing, and he could barely breathe. Ten minutes after the call to 911, he was on his way to the nearest emergency room in an ambulance. There an electrocardiogram and blood tests provided the big shock: Gerry hadn't suffered a heart attack at all. The hospital doctor reassured him: "Physically, you are fine. Your problems are psychological in origin."

Gerry's experience is not unusual. For at least a quarter of all patients who enter hospitals with suspected heart attacks, physicians can find no physical cause for their symptoms. But it is a mistake to dismiss such occurrences as "just psychosomatic," because that minimizes the importance of the mind's effects on the body's well-being. Studies in psychosomatics, the area of medicine that deals with diseases and complaints that are at least partly psychologically based, find that one everyday aspect of modern life stands out in a startling variety of physical ailments: stress. [*For a list of related ills, see box on page 67.*] Worse, extreme emotional distress—caused by the death of a spouse, a furious quarrel, a natural disaster such as an earthquake, even looming

BRYAN MULLENNIX *Stone* Getty Images

The Hostile Heart

To evaluate your overall tendency toward stressful hostility, use the Minnesota Multiphasic Personality Inventory Anger Content Scale. Answer true or false to each question:

T   F

1. At times I feel like **swearing**.

2. At times I feel like **smashing** things.

3. Often I can't understand why I've been so **irritable and grouchy**.

4. At times I feel like picking a **fistfight** with someone.

5. I easily become **impatient** with people.

6. I am often said to be **hotheaded**.

7. I am often so **annoyed** when someone tries to get ahead of me in a line of people that I speak to that person about it.

8. I have at times had to be **rough** with people who were rude or annoying.

9. I am often sorry because I am so **irritable and grouchy**.

10. It makes me **angry** to have people hurry me.

11. I am very **stubborn**.

12. Sometimes I get so **angry and upset** I don't know what comes over me.

13. I have gotten **angry** and broken furniture or dishes when I was drinking.

14. I have become so angry with someone that I have felt as if I would **explode**.

15. I've been so angry at times that I've **hurt someone** in a physical fight.

16. I almost never lose **self-control**.

0–5	Anger is not a problem.
6–10	Anger level is moderate; work on ways to relax.
11–16	Anger level is a concern; your health may suffer the consequences if corrective measures are not taken.

heavy deadlines at work—can trigger a real heart attack in a person who is already at risk.

In the U.S. alone, 1.5 million people suffer heart attacks every year, and more than 200,000 die. It is difficult to determine how many of those incidents might be attributed to stress, but it is clear that duress plays a role. Andrew Steptoe and Philip C. Strike of University College London recently reviewed a number of medical studies conducted between 1974 and 2004 that examined what people were doing and feeling in the hours before they had a heart attack. Emotional stress was one of the most common triggers, they reported in the March/April issue of *Psychosomatic Medicine*. For example, in one study of 224 patients, more than half said they had been very upset or under stress in the 24 hours before their heart attack.

Mind over Matter

How can your head hurt your heart? To answer that question, it helps to take a look at what happens in the body when you are experiencing stress. Imagine you are ambling across a street when a car unexpectedly rounds the corner without stopping, barreling toward you. Heart pounding, legs pumping, you dash out of harm's way. What just happened?

As your brain recognizes imminent danger, your body undergoes several changes. Stress hormones—epinephrine, norepinephrine, glucocorticoids—pour into your bloodstream, preparing you for a "fight or flight" response. To conserve energy for your leg muscles, nonessentials such as your digestive tract shut down. Your heart rate increases, to deliver oxygen and energy to your thighs and calves. Veins throughout the circulatory system constrict, as when you squeeze a water hose, propelling blood back to the heart more vigorously. That returning blood slams into heart walls, which in turn snap back with greater force, like a stretched rubber band. Arteries relax, increasing blood flow from the heart to those needy muscles.

Such physical reactions are helpful when you are bolting from a careless driver—or when early humans had to flee a hungry predator. And small stresses actually have an upside, because they sharpen our attention, making us feel focused and alert. (Think of playing a challenging quiz game or watching an exciting whodunit.)

But stress also arises frequently from the everyday hassles of modern life, as we run late to that meeting, fret about getting the kids to a play date across town or worry about getting all the details just right in time for tonight's dinner par-

HARVEY B. SIMON *Harvard Men's Health Watch*

Heart at Risk

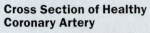

Cross Section of Healthy Coronary Artery

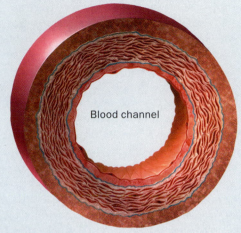

Blood channel

Artery Affected by Plaque

Narrowed channel at risk for blockage

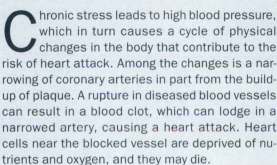

Chronic stress leads to high blood pressure, which in turn causes a cycle of physical changes in the body that contribute to the risk of heart attack. Among the changes is a narrowing of coronary arteries in part from the build-up of plaque. A rupture in diseased blood vessels can result in a blood clot, which can lodge in a narrowed artery, causing a heart attack. Heart cells near the blocked vessel are deprived of nutrients and oxygen, and they may die.

ty. We are especially susceptible when we feel that conditions are out of our control despite our struggles. The result is that our bodies keep working in overdrive far more than our evolutionary history has shaped us to do. Chronic stress can lead to high blood pressure. This hypertension, in turn, adds to a vicious cycle of physical changes that can tip the balance for people at risk, contributing to the onset of arrhythmia (irregular heartbeat, in which distended muscle chambers cannot efficiently pump out blood) or heart attack. In a heart attack, a clump of plaque lodges in a small vessel in the heart. The resulting blockage deprives nearby cells of nutrients and oxygen, starving them [*see box above*].

Stress experiments have revealed the mental mechanisms involved. In the 1990s James E. Skinner, now at the Vicor Technologies laboratory in Bangor, Pa., investigated which brain regions play a role. He worked with pigs, beginning by tying off one coronary artery to imitate the condition of a patient with coronary artery disease. Then he implanted cooling elements at specific spots to block nerve impulses running from the frontal lobe, the location of higher-reasoning centers in the brain, to areas involved in emotional reactions and in mediating excitatory hormones: the amygdala, hypothalamus, brain stem and sympathetic nervous system. When the pigs without nerve blocks were exposed to severe psychosocial stress—such as being put in entirely new, alarming surroundings—they often experienced fatal fibrillation, a condition in which the heart contracts erratically and does not pump blood. Similarly, electrical stimulation of certain parts of the frontal lobe in the pigs elicited a rap-

(The Authors)

MICHAEL FELD is a physician and freelance science writer in Cologne, Germany. JOHANN CASPAR RÜEGG is professor emeritus of physiology at the University of Heidelberg in Germany.

id heart rate and arrhythmias, in some cases leading to cardiac arrest. The pigs whose nerves had been blocked by cold, however, were spared.

Head to Heart

So what are the important emotional factors? In the early 1900s Hungarian-American psychoanalyst and psychiatrist Franz Gabriel Alexander, now often called the father of psychosomatics, played a leading role in identifying emotional tension as a significant cause of physical illness. Alexander and other pioneers in the field believed that disorders such as ulcers, high blood pressure, neurodermatitis and asthma were the body's reaction to chronic tension and psychological stress. Following in the footsteps of psychoanalysts, they held that certain individuals—who suppressed conflicts and emotions—were predisposed to develop ailments as a result. This point of view has fallen out of favor today, as purported links between certain personality types and diseases have been refuted. For example, many studies have shown that the melancholy "cancer personality" is just a myth. On the other hand, a given person's style of dealing with problems does matter.

That is what heart specialists Meyer Friedman and Ray Rosenman concluded in 1974, after conducting a multiyear study of people with so-called Type A personalities. They claimed these individuals—whose behavior is characterized by ambition, competitiveness and impatience—have

the pinnacle of the corporate hierarchy have greater control over their day-to-day working lives than their minions. Middle-ranking employees are more likely to suffer a special kind of stress, called the negative affect. People with this sensitivity disorder exhibit above-average levels of anxiety and depression. After a multiyear study of the negative affect in men and women, Bruce C. Jonas and James F. Lando of the Centers for Disease Control and Prevention reported in the April 2000 *Psychosomatic Medicine* that such chronically stressed people are twice as likely to have hypertension as normal individuals.

Men who explode with anger or expect the worst from people may punish their own bodies as well. Such men are more likely to develop a type of arrhythmia, says an article in the March 2004 issue of *Circulation*. Feelings of hostility, for example, made men 30 percent more likely to develop the condition. Other studies have shown that a strong adverse emotion such as anger doubles the risk of heart attack during the next couple of hours. [*See box on page 64 to find out if hostility might be a problem for you.*]

Irritation and fury are not the only threats to diseased coronary arteries. Nancy Frasure-Smith of McGill University believes that depression also seriously prejudices the chances of heart patients for recovery. Depression, in turn, can result from chronic uncontrollable stress, as well as from a previous heart attack. Victims often suffer from

> ## Men who explode with anger or expect the worst from people may punish their own bodies as well.

a considerably higher risk of heart attacks. In several additional studies, researchers sought a comprehensive evaluation of Friedman and Rosenman's belief; they were not able to provide confirmation. Yet the aggression and hostility exhibited by Type As contribute to higher levels of stress and its deleterious effects. And although Type As do not necessarily have an increased lifetime risk of having a heart attack, their short-tempered, impatient behavior makes it more likely that they will have a heart attack sooner, according to a study in the May/June 2003 issue of *Psychosomatic Medicine* by John E. J. Gallacher of the University of Wales College of Medicine.

Many top executives may be Type As, but simply being a Master of the Universe does not raise the risk of heart attack, perhaps because those at

inner hopelessness, such as fears of being unable to meet challenges in their work or personal lives. And loss of a beloved and trusted partner can literally break someone's heart: as long ago as 1969 Colin Murray Parkes, a British doctor, showed that widows and widowers suffered greatly increased mortality.

Looking on the Bright Side

As the work with the pigs showed, the frontal brain seems important in fibrillation and apparently is connected to the nerve cell bodies of the sympathetic nervous system in the spinal cord. Through this connection, the human mind ought to be able to influence heart function in a positive manner. Relaxation techniques such as autogenic training may possibly utilize this mechanism.

Mental Illnesses

According to current scientific thinking, the following disorders are among those believed to be at least partially caused psychosomatically:

Gastrointestinal system: Eating disorders (anorexia, bulimia, psychogenic obesity), constipation, irritable bowel syndrome, gastric ulcers

Cardiovascular system: High blood pressure (hypertension), syncope (fainting spells), cardiovascular heart disease, arrhythmia, heart attack

Airways: Asthma, nervous cough

Psychosomatic pains: Headaches, abdominal pains, soft-tissue rheumatism, certain muscular pains (myalgia)

Ear, nose and throat: Dizziness, hearing problems, tinnitus, swallowing problems

Endocrine system: Diabetes, psychosomatic dwarfism

Reproductive system: Male dysfunction, menstrual cycle disturbances, false pregnancy

Skin: Neurodermatitis, psychogenic pruritus, possibly psoriasis

---

Along with targeted stress management, such methods may improve the survival chances of heart patients more than daily exercise, as suggested by James A. Blumenthal of the Duke University Medical Center in 1997.

Psychotherapy's positive influence on bodily processes is especially evident in studies of pain patients. Neuropsychologist Pierre Rainville of the University of Montreal set up a therapeutic study based on suggestion, called guided imaging. Using positron-emission tomography (PET) imaging, he discovered that a brain region responsible for the conscious awareness of pain, the anterior cingulate gyrus, would become less active—merely because of spoken words.

Another means to break free of the self-reinforcing cycle of heart disease, stress and depression is cognitive behavioral therapy. Patients learn to give more weight to positive events in their lives than to negative ones [see "Treating Depression: Pills or Talk?" by Steven D. Hollon, Michael E. Thase and John C. Markowitz; SCIENTIFIC AMERICAN MIND, Premier Issue, 2004]. A strong social network, as well as contact with trusted individuals, helps people to overcome stress, too. Heart disease patients who are married or in stable relationships have longer average life expectancies.

Two other important ingredients to reversing cardiovascular disease are developing more healthful eating habits and exercising regularly. Dean Ornish and his colleagues at the University of California at San Francisco tracked the progress of patients with coronary artery disease who ate low-fat vegetarian diets and got regular exercise. The subjects stopped smoking, and they sought to bring calm to their lives through stress management training and group therapy. After a year, the condition of their coronary arteries had improved noticeably.

Is the power of the brain supreme when it comes to affecting physical well-being, or does the body's health sway our mental states? Both usually go hand in hand: body and mind are bound up, inseparably, in a continual feedback loop. The scientific knowledge gained in recent years teaches us that just as corporeal phenomena can change our minds and spirits, it works in the other direction as well: thoughts and emotions can cause real changes to our bodies.

(Further Reading)

◆ **Why Zebras Don't Get Ulcers.** Robert M. Sapolsky. Henry Holt and Company (Owl Books), 2004.
◆ American Heart Association Web site is at **www.americanheart.org**

Brian Wilson: A Cork on the Ocean

The rise and fall of the Beach Boys leader shows how crucial the brain's executive function is to creativity

By Brian Levine

What differentiates mere talent from creative genius? No one knows for sure. We do know, however, that many artistic advances and scientific discoveries come from men and women in their 20s—just old enough to have sufficient technical skills yet young enough to be unencumbered by the habits of older generations.

Psychological studies also indicate that highly creative people share an elevated risk of serious mental illness. For certain individuals, such ailments may actually contribute to their soaring achievements. Yet often the same condition eventually ruins their inventiveness and their lives. Perhaps no story better exemplifies how mental illness can free up creativity, then crush it, than that of Brian Wilson.

By age 22 Wilson had already invented a new form of American folk music, achieving tremendous success with his group, the Beach Boys. From 1962 to 1965 the Beach Boys had 16 top-40 hits, including "Surfin'

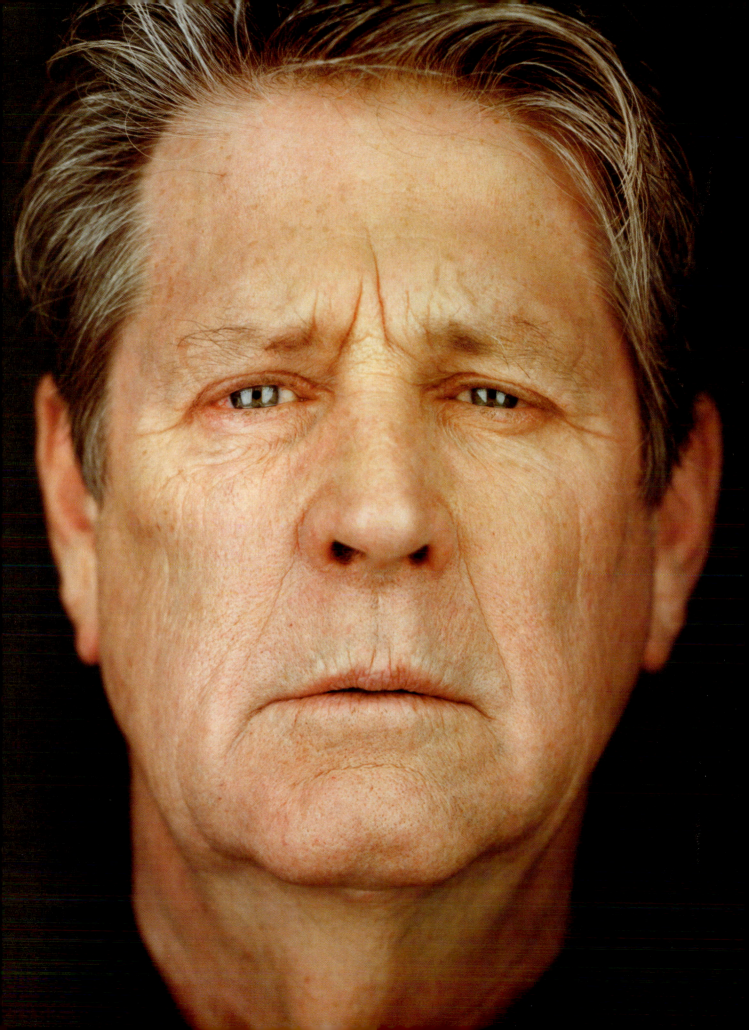

Brian Wilson (*at left*) was the primary writer, arranger and producer for the Beach Boys, who by 1965 had more than a dozen top hits, such as "Surfin' USA" and "I Get Around."

USA," "Little Deuce Coupe" and "I Get Around." Wilson, the group's primary writer, arranger and producer, then expanded his musical landscape with the Beach Boys' 1966 record *Pet Sounds*. The album altered the course of modern pop with its novel studio techniques, complex harmonic and rhythmic structures drawn from jazz and classical music, unusual instrumentation, and substantive themes of introspection and vulnerability. The legendary conductor and composer Leonard Bernstein called Wilson one of the greatest composers of the 20th century, and Paul McCartney of the Beatles cited *Pet Sounds* as the major influence for the group's own inventive landmark album in 1967, *Sgt. Pepper's Lonely Hearts Club Band*.

Unfortunately, the importance of Wilson's work was soon overshadowed in the popular consciousness by his steady and very public mental decline. In his early 20s, the typical age of onset for many psychotic disorders, social discomfort, depression and paranoia gave way to frank hallucinations and delusions. Over the following decade his condition progressed, and for a period of years he was unable to function con-

sistently as a member of society, much less at his previous level as a hit-record producer.

Progressive mental illness such as that experienced by Wilson causes a breakdown in "executive function"—the ability of the brain's frontal lobes to plan, coordinate and execute, much the way a CEO would direct the operations of a business. Cognitive neuroscientists are still debating the definition of executive function and its influence on behavior. But Wilson's case provides powerful evidence of its sway. Today, 30 years after his decline, Wilson has reemerged as a healthier individual and has returned to making music. His incredible story shows how executive function can set creativity free, how its demise can subsequently cripple that creativity and the ability to negotiate daily life, and how proper treatment and support by psychiatrists and loved ones can create ways to compensate—in Wilson's case, allowing him to make a comeback.

"Til I Die"

Neuroscientists maintain that the frontal lobes mediate a collection of high-level cognitive processes that enable us to control and direct lower-level processes. These executive functions allow us to transform a jumbled heap of puzzle pieces into a coherent picture. Think about preparing to go on a major trip. Your brain's CEO, working from the frontal lobes, sequences and prioritizes the many steps that must be performed, generating a plan to accomplish your goal and coming up with new tactics when circumstances change [*see box on page 73*].

Because the frontal lobes interact with multiple brain systems, executive functions are highly sensitive to brain disease, psychiatric disorders and substance abuse. Despite their central role and vulnerabilities, however, executive functions are not as well understood or appreciated as other mental capacities, such as memory and perception, which are more easily assessed in the lab. And because demands for executive functions are greatest in unstructured, novel situations, patients with executive difficulties often appear normal when taking routine psychological and neurological tests. Executive dysfunction is therefore often not diagnosed,

even in people who are seriously disabled by it.

The creative innovations heard on *Pet Sounds* coincided with the onset of Wilson's psychosis, which is characterized by a loosening of linkages between ideas. (This article is based on publicly available information, such as the authoritative books *The Beach Boys*, by David Leaf, and *The Nearest Faraway Place: Brian Wilson, the Beach Boys, and the Southern California Experience*, by Timothy White; documentaries such as *A&E Biography*; media interviews with Wilson himself—notably *Larry King Live* in 2004—as well as other sources. I have not talked to Wilson, nor have I seen his medical records, but the many sources converge on a description that experts would recognize as psychosis.)

Mental illness does not make a person creative. But certain individuals who are endowed with artistic vision and particular technical skills can, at times, transform the loosening of linkages into inspired artistic associations. These novel associations can be difficult for the individual to harness, however, because a person

A young Wilson, shown here in 1966, held in his mind intricate arrangements of many instruments and vocal harmonies, instructed older musicians to perform each part in the studio, then wove them together electronically, a masterful feat of executive function.

Once psychosis took root, Wilson had only intervals of creativity; his weight ballooned, he seldom performed, and he confined himself to his bed for long periods.

1964 on a plane flight to Houston, when he suffered a nervous breakdown. He subsequently stopped touring with the Beach Boys so that he could focus his attention on writing and studio work for the band, avoiding the stress of the road. He used the Wrecking Crew for the instrumental recording sessions, the same studio musicians employed by his idol, Phil Spector, who defined the role of the modern record producer with hits by the Crystals and the Ronettes, such as "Da Doo Ron Ron." Wilson's new work, appearing in 1965 on the next two albums, *The Beach Boys Today!* and *Summer Days (and Summer Nights!!)*, introduced elements that later came together in fully realized form on *Pet Sounds.*

To create *Pet Sounds,* Wilson enlisted a new collaborator, Tony Asher, to assist with lyrics intended to depart from the previous themes of surfing, girls and cars. Wilson constructed songs at the piano, beginning with "feels" or fragments of music representing a certain mood. By the time he entered the recording studio, he had a full arrangement in his mind that he then deconstructed by teaching musicians their parts one instrument at a time—from strings, horns and accordions to a water jug, bicycle bells and the theremin, the electronic gizmo responsible for spooky sounds in old horror movies and later made famous in the Beach Boys' song "Good Vibrations." Indeed, Wilson often demonstrated the parts himself, because he could play nearly all the instruments. Outtake recordings of Wilson working in the studio (which were included in the 1996 *Pet Sounds Sessions* box set) give an impression of a 23-year-old visionary leader directing the older and more experienced studio musicians to realize his artistic vision.

with psychosis is betrayed by his own disordered perceptions. It is a frighteningly lonely disease, which Wilson perhaps knowingly portrayed in 1971 when he wrote "Til I Die." The song's lush music, reminiscent of the sea, stands in stark juxtaposition to the lyrics: "I'm a cork on the ocean / Floating over the raging sea.... I'm a leaf on a windy day / Pretty soon I'll be blown away...."

Wilson had reached a breaking point in late

The last elements to be laid down on the album were the Beach Boys' vocals. No one but Wilson knew how the pieces would fit together until he assembled them at the final stage of production, when something spiritual emerged. As the late Timothy White, editor in chief of *Billboard* magazine throughout the 1990s, wrote in the liner notes to *Pet Sounds Sessions,* "What shines brightest behind, within and above the peal of Brian's exquisite material is the presence of the thing not named: an unswayable belief in the enduring power of one's better self."

(The Author)

BRIAN LEVINE is senior scientist at the Baycrest Center for Geriatric Care's Rotman Research Institute in Toronto and associate professor of psychology and medicine (neurology) at the University of Toronto. He is also an amateur musician and Brian Wilson fan.

The Brain's "CEO"

The role of executive function in human behavior is to coordinate the many brain activities needed to set goals, make plans to attain those goals, organize steps to carry out those plans, and ensure that the desired outcomes are achieved. This capacity can be likened to that of a company's chief executive officer. Psychologists are not in full agreement, but most acknowledge that multiple executive functions are mediated by the frontal lobes. The ones described below are engaged often.

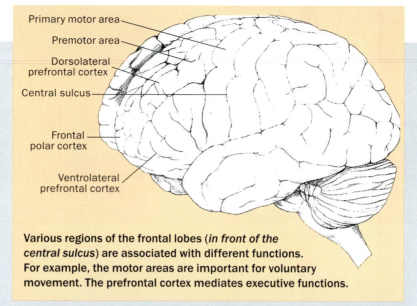

Various regions of the frontal lobes (*in front of the central sulcus*) are associated with different functions. For example, the motor areas are important for voluntary movement. The prefrontal cortex mediates executive functions.

Abstract thinking. Discerning relations among stimuli—seeing the forest for the trees—depends on abstract thinking. Imagine being asked to group into two sets of objects a pair of scissors, a water glass, an ax and a wheelbarrow. You might decide that the scissors and the water glass go together because they are used indoors, whereas the ax and wheelbarrow are used outdoors.

Attention shifting. Can you find another grouping? Scissors and axes cut, glasses and wheelbarrows contain. Many people with executive deficits find it hard to shift attention and inflexibly hold on to their original perceptions and behaviors, even when the usefulness of these associations has long expired.

Information manipulation. Nearly all higher-order cognitive operations require the real-time manipulation of information held in short-term memory. To prepare for a dinner party, a host has to juggle multiple timetables of when different foods will be cooked as well as consider the likes and dislikes of guests.

Planning and foresight. Preparing for a vacation requires foresight and analysis of the conditions and needs at the destination, which may be very different from the conditions and needs at home. A patient with executive dysfunction is often unable to escape the present to form a mental model of a future that is different.

Monitoring and error correction. These processes are engaged when results do not correspond with intentions. This effect could be seen, for example, in a woman who drives to a special bakery to buy a pie for a dinner party she is throwing that evening and finds it is closed. She might go to another bakery on the other side of town without considering that the trip would not allow her to get back home until long after the guests had arrived.

Decision making. Consider a man who is having trouble making ends meet. He could cut expenses or increase income, either path requiring him to weigh options, arrive at a decision and see it through. Patients with executive difficulties cannot settle on a choice, particularly in situations where the correct response is not obvious or previously learned. They may blindly follow other people's suggestions, which is why they can be easily exploited.

Inhibition. Automatic responses can be unhelpful or even harmful. Imagine you have just won a major award; your reaction would be to tell everyone your news. But waiting until other finalists are properly informed of their loss requires inhibition.

Social functioning. Failure to appropriately process or output social cues can have devastating consequences. The main concern of one frontal lobe dementia patient, on seeing that his wife was cut and bleeding badly from an accident involving a power tool, was that the tool be cleaned as soon as possible.   —B.L.

Recording multiple instrumental and vocal tracks and fitting them into a coherent whole relies on manipulating many streams of information held in short-term memory, a key executive function. Whereas other producers at the time recorded relatively simple songs in a single "take" performed by the entire group, Wilson held in his mind intricate symphonic arrangements and harmonies, recorded parts separately, then later put together the pieces of the puzzle. The song "Good

Vibrations," dubbed a "pocket symphony" by Wilson and released as a single just after *Pet Sounds*, was recorded in 17 sessions at various studios. The hit, which in music polls ranks as one of the greatest pop songs ever, represented the ultimate marriage of creativity with executive functions, prompting a key transition in popular music in which the studio itself was added to the impresario's quiver.

How was Wilson able to accomplish these monumental feats of vision and concentration while suffering from serious mental illness? Psychotic symptoms are not static; they wax and

Improved therapy for schizoaffective disorder, along with support from his friends and second wife, Melinda, enabled Wilson to return to active touring after 30 years.

wane. Wilson's productivity was most likely greatest when his symptoms were in remission—when novel creative associations could be screened, manipulated and coherently integrated by his musical and executive powers.

Two Years in Bed

These powers were soon eclipsed by Wilson's progressive mental illness. The balance between inspiration and the cognitive capacity to realize that inspiration had shifted by 1967, as he and lyricist Van Dyke Parks were putting together *Smile,* an integrated set of album cuts centered on American culture and history.

A good indication of how Wilson's capabilities were slipping involves "output monitoring." This executive function gives someone the ability to compare his actions to his intentions—to screen for errors and bad ideas. Wilson used unusual but successful sound ideas on *Pet Sounds,* such as bicycle bells to invoke themes of lost childhood, but his quest during *Smile* became bizarre—outfit-

ting his musicians with fire hats during the recording of "Mrs. O'Leary's Cow" or infamously placing his piano in a sandbox. Yet because by this time he had been labeled as a "genius," people around him often indulged his eccentricities rather than confronting them as symptoms of serious sickness. Evidence of faulty monitoring can also be heard in the original *Pet Sounds* recording, in which Wilson, usually the consummate perfectionist, allowed background chatter from the studio to creep into the final mix.

Once he had completed *Smile*'s elements, Wilson seemed unable to fit them together. Parks eventually left the project, according to several accounts. Capitol Records was pressuring Wilson to produce something. But emotionally fragile and without support from his bandmates, he scrapped the *Smile* project in mid-1967. That summer acid rocker Jimi Hendrix literally sounded the death knell for surf music at the Monterey Pop Festival.

Wilson's mental health steadily deteriorated, with occasional bouts of suicidal depression and psychosis. His drug habit, which could have been an attempt to self-treat his symptoms (common among patients with psychosis), expanded into heroin and especially cocaine use. He demonstrated intervals of creativity, but he never matched the breadth and complexity of his earlier work. He had two young children but was unable to assume a parental role and separated from his wife in 1978. By the early 1980s Wilson's weight had ballooned to more than 300 pounds, and he confined himself to his bed for two and a half years. Although there were periods of hospitalization and detox, treatment was not sustained. Wilson's public appearances were inconsistent at best.

Because of his tremendous notoriety, Wilson's mental troubles soon became part of the public consciousness. The media mocked him as some kind of nut. Viewed from the patient's perspective, however, staying in bed makes perfect sense when one is immersed in a warped reality.

As is often the case with patients who have executive dysfunction, Wilson's compromised state left him vulnerable to exploitation. His own psychologist, Eugene Landy, directed his life and career in the mid-1970s and then again from 1983 to 1991, according to several accounts and to Wilson's second wife, Melinda, during the Larry King interview. Although Landy was successful in isolating Wilson from illicit drugs and in helping him to lose weight, he also fostered a dependent relationship: he administered psychotropic drugs to Wilson, acted as his business adviser, and even attempted to collaborate with the artist on songwriting and singing. Wilson's family sued for conservatorship in 1990, and the issue was settled the following year. The court severed contact between Wilson and Landy, who had by then already surrendered his license to practice psychology in California to the state's Board of Medical Quality Assurance after conceding that he had unlawfully administered drugs to Wilson.

Creative Prosthesis

Throughout the 1990s Wilson received more conventional treatment, including medication and psychotherapy. He settled into a stable marriage. During the Larry King interview, Wilson and Melinda revealed that he had been diag-

but it weakened for some reason—and I lost the ability to concentrate enough to follow through." Wilson is also now appearing live, sitting in front of a keyboard, although he does not play much. His singing, though still serviceable, is inconsistent. None of this really matters to his fans, however, who come for Wilson's legend and mystique.

Wilson reached a creative zenith in his early adulthood in spite of (and perhaps partly because of) his mental illness, which eventually robbed him of the cognitive abilities required to create art and nearly destroyed him. Wilson's comeback demonstrates that with proper treatment and support, individuals with mental illness can function at a high level in areas of their expertise, even if their symptoms persist.

During the painful interim, life took down

(**Wilson's comeback** shows that with proper treatment, a life lost to psychosis can rebound.)

nosed with schizoaffective disorder, a combination of psychosis and abnormal mood. With support from his wife and musical colleagues, Wilson was reemerging in public, recording albums and performing as a solo artist, accompanied by musicians from the Los Angeles band the Wondermints and former Beach Boys guitarist Jeff Foskett.

Improved treatment of schizoaffective disorder has helped Wilson and many others. After more than 30 years he returned his attention to *Smile,* widely considered one of the greatest unreleased albums in contemporary music. Wilson appeared comfortable in the recording studio—executive dysfunction does not directly compromise memory or acquired musical skills. But it does affect the capacity to flexibly deploy them, particularly in an unstructured situation where there are no clear right or wrong answers, as in the creation of an album.

Wilson released *Smile* in 2004, at age 62, to worldwide acclaim. Its success is attributable to the quality of the original material and to the guidance and support of others who helped Wilson assemble the pieces—people who provide a prosthesis for Wilson's frontal lobes. According to Timothy White's book, Wilson had recognized this need as early as 1976, when in a recording session he said, "Something happened to my concentration—I don't know exactly what,

other family members in the Beach Boys. Wilson's brother Dennis, the heart of the band, drowned in 1983, and brother Carl, the guitarist with the angelic voice, died of cancer in 1998. And whereas *Pet Sounds* was so perfectly poised in time, the political, cultural and musical milieu that spawned *Smile* almost immediately became a casualty of violence, war and lost innocence.

To paraphrase renowned psychologist and memory researcher Endel Tulving of the Rotman Research Institute in Toronto, time's arrow runs straight, but memory endows us with the capacity to bend that arrow into a loop, to revise the past in our minds to regain, even if in fantasy, that which was lost. If Wilson's public resurrection bolsters this hope, then *Smile* 2004, bending time's arrow back 37 years, codifies it. Perhaps, then, *Smile* fulfills a larger purpose beyond its lush and creative music: the need to believe that that which was lost can be regained. **M**

(Further Reading)

◆ **Adult Clinical Neuropsychology: Lessons from Studies of the Frontal Lobes.** D. T. Stuss and B. Levine in *Annual Review of Psychology,* Vol. 53, pages 401–433; 2002.
◆ **Forty Lives in the Bebop Business: Mental Health in a Group of Eminent Jazz Musicians.** G. I. Wills in *British Journal of Psychiatry,* Vol. 183, No. 3, pages 255–259; 2003.
◆ **Wouldn't It Be Nice: Brian Wilson and the Making of the Beach Boys' *Pet Sounds.*** C. L. Granata. Chicago Review Press, 2003.

The collision damaged his forebrain.
Surgeons saved it.
But they never checked his pituitary,
and he is no longer the man he was

PERSONALITY
CRASH

By Felicitas Witte

The sun had just risen as Dan Shelby began pedaling his bicycle down a main thoroughfare in Philadelphia. The computer programmer had to get to work early, and the traffic was still light. Seeing no oncoming cars, he quickly stuck out his arm as a signal and made an abrupt left onto the cross street.

DOUG MENUEZ Corbis

He hadn't spotted the sedan already bounding up that road into the intersection, right at him. Dan's head crashed into the windshield, and he crumpled to the pavement, unconscious and bleeding.

This is how witnesses describe the accident of September 17, 2002 (names and locations of this real case have been changed). Despite the bike helmet, Shelby's brain was so damaged that he fell into a coma. He had severe craniocerebral trauma (CCT)—widespread injury to the brain and its nerves, especially to the frontal lobes. Half of all patients with severe CCT die within

sight is more common than the medical community realizes. And it is an understandable lapse: after all, doctors are attempting to save these patients' lives; most hormonal glands are just not that critical.

What Wife?

After several surgeries, ongoing treatment in the intensive care unit stabilized Shelby's brain and body. He emerged from the coma after 20 days, and many weeks later he was transferred to a rehab clinic. There he could not remember the accident or anything from the days prior to it. He

> (After the accident Dan was **easily irritated** yet dissolved into tears at the slightest conflict.)

several hours. Many of those who do not will stay in the coma and, if they come out, may have serious losses of memory and other mental functions. Shelby's doctors did not know if he would emerge or what shape his brain would be in. Unfortunately, his case was not unique: bike, car and other violent accidents cause CCT in tens of thousands of victims each year.

Within hours Shelby's neurosurgeons recognized that the cyclist had suffered a frontal brain contusion with cerebral hemorrhage. They quickly began operating to relieve surging fluid and inflammation in the affected area. The fact that a pea-size gland deep in the interior of his head was also damaged escaped them. That over-

did remember what was going through his head when he first regained consciousness: he heard a small band playing Christmas music.

As rehab progressed, day by day Shelby felt as though his life was beginning again. Each bit of progress was a quiet triumph. But Shelby's wife had a hard time sharing his joy. Despite her daily visits, her husband did not recognize her. She was shocked when he asked who she was. Shelby's psychological functions were sluggish; his emotions seemed random. Such symptoms are common in CCT victims, and Mrs. Shelby tried to be patient, showing excitement as her husband learned to walk and brush his teeth again. After a trying six months, Shelby did manage to piece together some recognition of his family and former life. His doctors sent him home, and he looked forward to reestablishing relationships with his wife and two young daughters.

But the much anticipated normalcy did not return. The family experienced a husband and father who was a changed man. He was easily irritated yet dissolved into tears at the slightest conflict, and one morning he became so enraged that he threw his coffee cup at the wall. His wife found he had virtually no libido and could not keep an erection. After frustrating attempts to fire up their love life, the couple agreed to a platonic relationship.

During this period Shelby continued to go to rehab and started occupational therapy—mental exercises intended to gradually restore the capabilities he needed to resume his programming job. There he realized that he could barely concentrate. He frequently interrupted whichever

FAST FACTS
Pituitary Damage

1 >> **Neurosurgeons have many life-threatening complications to resolve in patients who have undergone a violent blow to the head.** The doctors can easily overlook hard-to-spot signs of trauma to the pituitary gland deep in the brain.

2 >> **The pituitary controls the release of numerous hormones.** People with untreated pituitary damage can have significant hormone imbalances and may therefore seem to take on new personalities. Many lose their libido, become irritable, fly into rages and yet also quickly fall into despair. They often have difficulty planning and making judgments.

3 >> **Simple blood tests can determine if the pituitary has been compromised.** Hormone therapies can restore balance and bring patients back to their old selves again.

Gland Master

The pea-size pituitary gland is located at the base of the brain. This "master gland" releases hormones (*red arrows*) that command other glands and organs crucial to basic bodily functions such as growth, temperature regulation and blood pressure. The glands and organs send feedback (*orange arrows*) to the pituitary and to the brain's hypothalamus (*yellow arrows*), which instructs the pituitary to raise or reduce its output of a given hormone. Injury to the pituitary can cause these physical and psychological complications:

- Low output of thyroid-stimulating hormone (TSH) to the thyroid gland can reduce the body's metabolic rate, possibly causing weight gain, shivering, fatigue or dry skin, and can prompt emotional mood swings.
- Deficiencies in follicle-stimulating hormone (FSH) and luteinizing hormone (LH) can undermine development of female eggs and male sperm, as well as reduce libido and bring on depression.
- Too little adrenocorticotropic hormone (ACTH) to the adrenal gland can lead to weakness, fatigue, apathy or anxiety.
- Growth hormones such as somatotrophic hormone (STH) control the production of muscle, bone and fat. Extreme shortages during development can result in dwarfism, oversupply in gigantism. Deficiencies in adults may cause apathy or depression and affect concentration power.
- The pituitary's posterior lobe secretes antidiuretic hormone, which regulates water retention by the kidneys, and oxytocin, which causes uterine contractions and affects mammary gland stimulation (*hormones not shown*). —*F.W.*

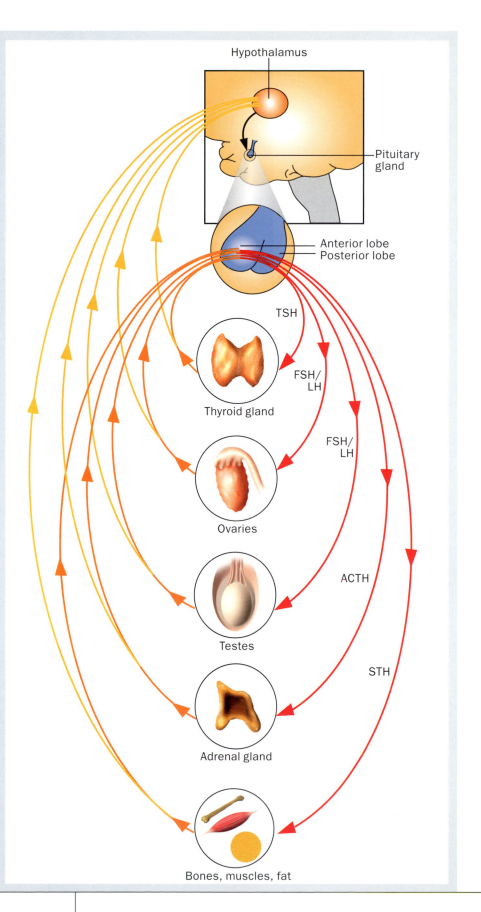

Hypothalamus

Pituitary gland

Anterior lobe
Posterior lobe

TSH

FSH/LH

FSH/LH

ACTH

STH

Thyroid gland

Ovaries

Testes

Adrenal gland

Bones, muscles, fat

SIGANIM

Pituitary damage can cause hormone deficiencies that leave victims incapable of sustaining relationships or handling stress.

therapist was speaking and then talked without stopping. He forgot what other people told him, and he got mad over minor hurdles.

Shelby's wife had an increasingly hard time handling her husband's change in personality. His memory of their relationship gradually returned, but he was still emotionally absent. She withdrew and, in the autumn of 2003, asked for a separation. Shortly thereafter Shelby moved into an apartment near downtown. Though sad, breakups are not uncommon after such a severe accident. Indeed, Shelby's case was somewhat typical for CCT patients. Damage to the frontal lobes in particular can lead to disorders in drive and behavior. Patients are virtually incapable of planning anything and have trouble judging the consequences of their own actions. They tend toward wild mood swings and, like little children, have a hard time controlling their anger. Many relationships cannot survive such a change.

Hormone Failure

A year after the accident Shelby began work again at his old company, on a reduced schedule. His co-workers were understanding; at first he was to focus on simple programs and small projects. But unlike before, the highly trained professional was no longer self-motivated and could not seem to figure out what needed to be done first. He had great difficulty completing his assignments.

Shelby asked his doctors frequently about his symptoms, but they told him the same thing each time: he was suffering from the usual late consequences of CCT. But Shelby could not reconcile himself to his condition. After two years he had had enough. His work was terrible; his sex life was unsatisfactory. He insisted to his doctors that

(The Author)

FELICITAS WITTE is a physician and freelance science writer in Mannheim, Germany.

something was not right. They readmitted him to a hospital.

Curious about the sexual dysfunction, doctors determined that Shelby had almost no testosterone, the male sex hormone. Surprised, they sent him for further hormone screening. The findings: several of his major glands were underproducing, and their deficiencies were all linked to the tiny pituitary gland at the foundation of his

Furthermore, hormone metabolism is almost always disturbed in the days following a severe accident, and the chaos does not necessarily have anything to do with trauma to the pituitary. For example, most women miss their menstrual cycle after CCT or other major head injuries. The production of thyroid hormones or growth hormones can also be inhibited because the brain cuts back on all metabolic processes that are not crucial to

(**Thanks to hormone therapy, Dan is his old self again, despite occasional limitations.**)

brain. This "master gland" releases hormones that command other glands and organs crucial to basic bodily functions. Low pituitary output was depressing Shelby's thyroid gland, in turn depressing his metabolism and making his emotions erratic. The sagging pituitary also suppressed his adrenal gland, leaving him fatigued, and limited his growth hormones, oddly enough reducing his concentration. And it cut his sex hormones, erasing his libido and triggering bouts of crying and depression. The doctors finally understood that the pituitary had been damaged in the accident, and it was releasing very little of the crucial messenger molecules that direct other hormonal systems of the body.

Because the pituitary gland is sheltered deep within the brain, physicians rarely think to look there for trauma. Until recently, it was the medical consensus that damage to the region was a rare complication of CCT, according to Guenter Stalla, an internist and neuroendocrinologist at the Max Planck Institute for Psychiatry in Munich. Few researchers had investigated this phenomenon, although a look back at the limited studies does show that people who died from CCT had impaired pituitary glands. And in recent investigations, researchers have found massive hormone disturbances in a third or more of CCT patients.

Stalla worries that many people who have recovered physically from CCT may be walking around with significant psychological, behavioral or relationship problems because their pituitary ills remain undiagnosed. Simple blood tests can determine if the master gland is compromised, but many physicians do not consider pituitary deficiencies because hormone levels do not play much of a role in the acute phase of treatment after an accident.

life. Generally, however, the body starts producing these hormones again after a few weeks.

Shelby's doctors might have been unconsciously figuring on that very trend. But ignoring a hormone deficiency could have fatal consequences, leaving the body unable to handle severe stress and perhaps allowing a traumatically sick person to die of shock, Stalla warns. Stalla and other neurologists are beginning to study how a doctor can recognize whether a patient is suffering from a debilitating pituitary disturbance. So far the investigators have found abnormally low levels of at least one hormone group in five of 17 head trauma patients, indicating that pituitary insufficiency may be more frequent than previously thought. In response, Stalla recommends that physicians test hormone levels of patients three months after an accident. Monthly tests thereafter may help rule in or rule out pituitary damage.

Once Shelby's hormone trouble had been diagnosed, he was given thyroid hormones, growth hormones, cortisol and sex hormones, and doctors continue to monitor those levels regularly to this day. Shelby says he has finally gotten back his original zest for life. And even though he sometimes notices mental limitations, he says he is also his old self at work again. He socializes in the evening, meets friends, plays sports and sees his daughters often. Now 40, Shelby has not yet found a new partner. But he is happy to be leading a nearly normal life. He is even riding to work, more cautiously, on his bike again. **M**

(**Further Reading**)

- ◆ **Neuroendocrine Dysfunction in the Acute Phase of Traumatic Brain Injury.** Amar Agha et al. in *Clinical Endocrinology,* Vol. 60, No. 5, pages 584–591; May 2004.
- ◆ The Pituitary Society offers information on disorders and doctors at **www.pituitarysociety.org/public**

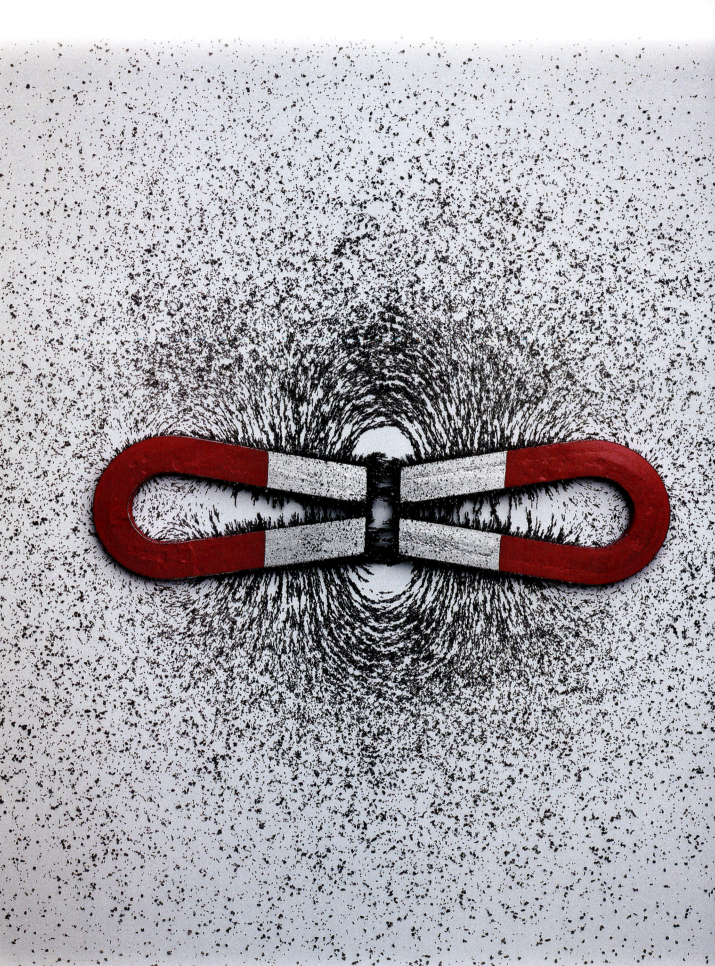

Magnetically stimulating the brain could lift depression and perhaps even boost creativity, but questions remain

BY HUBERTUS BREUER

A GREAT ATTRACTION

When American psychiatrist Mark S. George stepped into the elevator of a London hospital in 1990, he had no idea the short ride would transform his research career. A fellow passenger was having a giggling fit for no apparent reason. When George inquired about the outburst of merriment, the man replied that a doctor had held a magnetic coil against his head and that it had made his thumb twitch uncontrollably.

Even though the tale sounded a bit like quackery, George was curious. He contacted the doctor, who said he had stimulated the man's motor cortex, located at the top of the head, in hopes of seeing whether it would spark

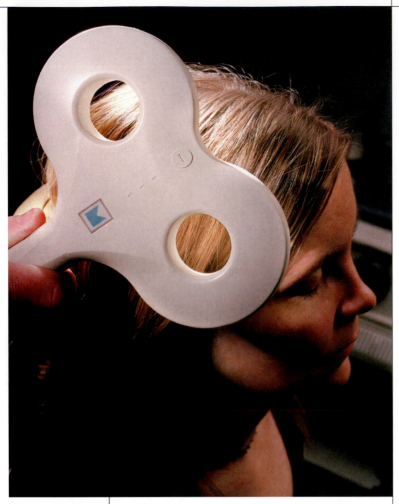

treatment with antidepressant medication had failed. George focused a strong magnetic field on the left prefrontal cortex—the region of the brain that is underactive in clinically depressed people—and found that the mood of two of his patients improved, at least for a few days.

Since that time, interest in transcranial magnetic stimulation, or TMS, has blossomed. Physicians have since reported success in curbing epileptic convulsions and even in reducing the notorious shakes of Parkinson's disease. Some investigators today also hope to awaken hidden creativity and heighten consciousness in the average person. Others are skeptical, however, because controlled trials have been few, and even George warns against touting the young technique as a panacea.

"It is still unclear exactly what this method does to the brain," he says, "and anything that has the power to heal can also certainly harm." It is worth noting, too, that although the U.S. Food and Drug Administration has approved TMS devices for diagnostic applications, it has not approved them for any kind of therapeutic use.

Better than Shock Treatment

The basic principle of TMS is simple. A coil of wire is placed near the head. Alternating current flowing through the coil induces a magnetic field with a strength of up to 2.5 teslas (one tesla is 20,000 times the strength of the earth's magnetic field). The field passes harmlessly through the skull and influences the electrical signals passing among neurons in the brain.

Physicians hold the coil close to whichever brain region they are interested in stimulating. One variation, known as repetitive transcranial magnetic stimulation (rTMS), is to switch the current on and off from one to 100 times a minute, which creates a series of magnetic impulses. This approach is often used in experiments on people with depression. Remarkably, rTMS can elicit two opposing reactions: a low frequency will block neural activity, yet higher frequencies will stimulate it. It is the stimulation that appears to lift the veil of depression, perhaps by promoting the release of important neurotransmitters, such as serotonin, which can raise activity in neurons to normal levels.

TMS appears to temporarily lift the veil of depression by promoting the release of certain neurotransmitters.

a signal to any muscles. The doctor had learned about what researcher Anthony T. Barker of the University of Sheffield in England did in the mid-1980s: Barker transmitted 4,000 amperes of current through a copper coil to create a strong, tight magnetic field, then held his homemade device against his own head. His thumb suddenly jerked up involuntarily. The magnetic field had obviously been strong enough to deliver a stimulus to the brain through the skull—"transcranially."

George asked the doctor if he had ever tried the device on the frontal regions of the cortex. The doctor replied no and wondered out loud why anyone would want to do that. When George returned to his laboratory at the Medical University of South Carolina, he proceeded to answer the question himself. He had a hunch that if the technique worked, it could perhaps help patients suffering from severe depression, for whom conventional

(Controlled trials have been few, and it is still unclear how the technique affects neurons.)

Targeted Stimulation

Localized brain cell excitation results from the use of a transcranial magnetic stimulation (TMS) machine. When researchers operate a TMS coil near a subject's scalp, a powerful and rapidly changing magnetic field passes safely and painlessly through skin and bone. Each brief pulse, lasting only microseconds, contains little energy. Because the strength of the magnetic field falls off rapidly with distance, it can penetrate only a few centimeters to the outer cortex of the brain (*top right*). The precisely located field induces electric current in nearby neurons, thus activating targeted regions of the brain (*bottom right*). A principal benefit of TMS is that it requires no direct electrical connection to the body, as is required for electroconvulsive therapy.

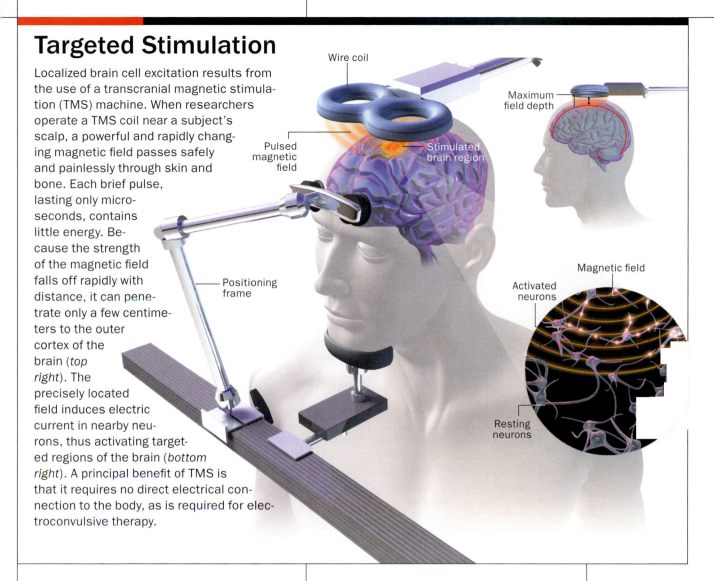

Wire coil

Pulsed magnetic field

Stimulated brain region

Positioning frame

Maximum field depth

Magnetic field

Activated neurons

Resting neurons

The magnetic wand offers several advantages over other therapeutic methods. It is noninvasive and painless. Subjects have reported no discomfort other than what they describe as a slight pull on the scalp. Mild headaches are common side effects, but they seem to be relieved readily with typical over-the-counter medication. The apparatus, however, makes a loud noise, which can be annoying. And a handful of patients have had seizures. Yet this seems, overall, more palatable than the side effects of the primary technique used on severely depressed patients who do not respond to medication—electroconvulsive therapy, better known as shock treatment. In this approach, a patient is given general anesthesia as well as muscle relaxants. A strong electrical impulse is delivered through electrodes on the patient's head, triggering a convulsion in the brain. This uncontrolled thunderstorm of neuronal firing relieves depression for a short time for roughly 80 percent of cases, which is encouraging, yet subjects also often experience heart palpitations as well as subsequent confusion and memory lapses.

The positive effects of TMS are intriguing. In 1999 Ehud Klein, a psychologist at the Rambam Medical Center in Haifa, Israel, led the largest study to date. Klein exposed 70 patients suffering from major depression to 10 daily sessions of repetitive TMS over a two-week period. Half received real TMS, and half received a sham version—the magnet was held at an angle that rendered the field ineffective. The mood of participants who had been properly exposed improved on the Hamilton Depression Rating Scale, used to assess symptoms. But no change was found for subjects who had sat under the ineffective coils.

TMS is still in an extended experimental

(The Author)

HUBERTUS BREUER is a science journalist in New York City and has a doctorate in philosophy.

BRYAN CHRISTIE DESIGN

stage, however. Only a few trials, involving a small number of test subjects, have been published; there has been little follow-up. The types of people, brain locations, coil configurations, and magnetic field strengths and frequencies have varied considerably, making it practically impossible to compare study results. Positive effects, if they exist, may result from a combination of all the variables, George says, "and I doubt that we've hit upon the most effective arrangement." A metastudy of depression trials also concluded there was no strong evidence of benefit.

Another deficit is that therapeutic effects seem to last only a few days to a few weeks. For example, Thomas Schlaepfer, a psychiatrist at the University of Bonn in Germany, was able to reduce obsessive behavior in one of his female patients. For years, the woman had found it necessary to perform a series of complicated rituals before she could pass through a doorway, but after a TMS session she was immediately able to walk from one room to the next with no hesitation. Unfortunately, she reverted to her old behavior after only a week.

Still, even this duration shows that the effect on neurons does not disappear as soon as the coil

Stimulating Topography

To show how TMS first concentrates and then spreads, Jarmo Ruohonen, now at Nexstim, Ltd., in Helsinki, Finland, used electroencephalographic sensors to track electrical activity after a TMS pulse. The diagrams show one subject's head as seen from above (the nose is at 12 o'clock). A magnetic pulse was initiated over the left-hand motor area. Positive electrical waves (*blue*) radiated around to the head's right side as negative potentials (*red*) convened in the left side. Beyond 29 milliseconds the activation pattern became complicated, in part because electrical activity had arisen in response to the subject's hearing the noise the TMS instrument makes.

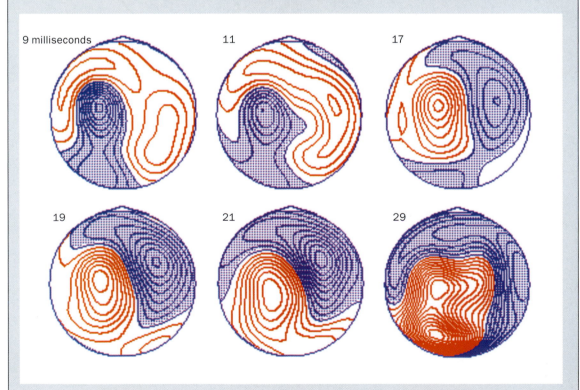

9 milliseconds   11   17

19   21   29

COURTESY OF JARMO RUOHONEN

is removed. The procedure does more than simply intervene among neurons; it somehow transforms the neuronal network for a time. Molecular studies by neuropsychologist Armand Hausmann of Innsbruck Medical University in Austria suggest that TMS stimulates neuronal factors that are known to aid in cell growth.

Devil in the Details

If TMS can promote neuron growth, then it could potentially help people who suffer from degenerative brain diseases such as Alzheimer's, although that is speculation. Strengthening neural networks means that TMS could perhaps promote cognition and creativity, too. These possibilities require some leaps of faith, but a smaller step can be gleaned from TMS's history thus far. The technique has been most widely used as a diagnostic tool to stimulate specific regions of the cortex, helping neurologists gauge their function.

When Alvaro Pascual-Leone, a brain researcher at Beth Israel Deaconess Medical Center in Boston, managed to direct a coil at the language center of his participants, they suddenly could not utter a single word. TMS literally left them speechless. Peter Eichhammer of the University of Regensburg in Germany has provided at least some relief for people who suffer from tinnitus—a persistent, even maddening ringing or buzzing in the brain. After five half-hour treatment cycles, some participants reported a substantial decrease in background noise, which for a few individuals lasted up to six months.

Other work is further on the fringe. George has an agreement with the U.S. Department of Defense to try to use magnetic stimulation to keep fighter pilots alert and attentive. The dream is a TMS helmet that will animate exhausted soldiers back into battle. Michael A. Persinger of Laurentian University in Ontario has wired magnetic coils inside a motorcycle helmet that he says has enabled experimental subjects to believe they sense the presence of a supernatural being; some have reported encounters with a guardian angel; still others state they have encountered Satan. As a result, Persinger suspects that spiritual experiences are nothing more than a product of our brains.

Your Inner Savant

More tangible, but equally elusive, is the notion that TMS could heighten creativity. Allan Snyder, director of the Center for the Mind in Canberra and Sydney, Australia, foresees a "thinking cap" that will help psychologically healthy individuals

attain unimagined heights of consciousness. He would like to awaken the slumbering genius in all of us with a kind of magnetic brain doping.

Snyder's inspiration comes from savants—autistic and other severely handicapped individuals who nonetheless display remarkable skills in certain cognitive areas. Some are gifted musicians, mathematical geniuses or outstanding artists. In most savants, the left hemisphere of the brain, considered to be the chief regulator for behavior, is chronically underactive. Snyder believes that the right side of the brain compensates with increased activity, bringing latent talents to the fore. He contends that temporarily switching off the left hemisphere with magnetic fields could allow pent-up creativity in the right hemisphere to spring forth. "I've always wanted to know what would happen if we could suddenly see the world without any censorship," Snyder says. He reports that he has temporarily slowed the left hemisphere's activity in test subjects and that their thinking became less reason-driven, less stuck in its tracks.

The popular media has seized on Snyder's work and made it appear that such sharp targeting of our brain is already a reality. But scientists harbor a number of well-founded objections to findings of anything that could be called heightened creative skills. Yet speculation about fanciful applications abound. For example, students could block a brain region responsible for anxiety before an exam, improving their performance. In theory, no part of one's mind would be shielded from magnetic influence. If true, could TMS make people always speak the truth, vote for a specific political party or even murder someone? Although such potential misuse of TMS may only be a threat in the distant future, this technology calls for ethical discussions today.

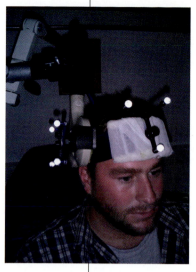

Researchers have magnetically suppressed the persistent buzzing sound in the brains of tinnitus sufferers, sometimes with lasting effects.

(Further Reading)

◆ **Transcranial Magnetic Stimulation for Treating Depression (Cochrane Review).** J.L.R. Martin et al. in *The Cochrane Library*; July 2001 and November 2004.
◆ **Stimulating the Brain.** Mark S. George in *Scientific American*, Vol. 289, No. 3, pages 66–73 (pages 46–53, international issue); September 2003.
◆ **Repetitive Transcranial Magnetic Stimulation for the Treatment of Depression: Systematic Review and Meta-analysis.** J. L. Martin et al. in *British Journal of Psychiatry*, Vol. 182, pages 480–491; 2003.

PETER EICHHAMMER *University of Regensburg*

A scandal over hidden data about adolescent suicide
lights a dark corner of our drug approval system
BY DAVID DOBBS

Antidepressants: Good Drugs or Good Marketing?

Pallbearers carry the coffin of Traci Johnson, a 19-year-old from Bensalem, Pa., who committed suicide this past February in an Eli Lilly research lab where she was a volunteer testing a new antidepressant, duloxetine.

DISCUSSION ABOUT the use of antidepressants by children, always a hot topic, boiled over in September when hearings revealed that both the drug industry and the Food and Drug Administration had hidden evidence about dangers associated with the most widely prescribed drugs, a class known as selective serotonin reuptake inhibitors. The analysis, which pharmaceutical companies failed to release to the public and which the FDA sat on for a year, indicated that these SSRIs double the suicide risk in depressed juveniles yet help no more children in trials than placebos do.

The high-profile congressional and FDA hearings were made all the more dramatic as parents recounted how their children had moved from moderate depression to suicide within days of starting SSRIs. Some of their children died during the year of delayed FDA action. Congressional subcommittee chair Representative Joe Barton of Texas lambasted the drug companies for withholding information and said the FDA's connivance suggested its initials stood for "foot-dragging and alibis." Even John Hayes, product team leader for Eli Lilly (whose Prozac was the one SSRI found both effective and safe) acknowledged the crisis with marked understatement, saying, "These hearings

(Results withheld by drugmakers and ignored by the FDA found that **SSRIs in juveniles provided only a placebo-level benefit** yet doubled suicidal tendencies.)

are evidence … there is a great deal of mistrust."

Given the stellar rise of SSRI antidepressants such as Prozac, Zoloft and Paxil, perhaps a fall was due. Since Prozac's introduction in 1988, SSRIs had been hailed for being as effective as earlier classes of antidepressants yet having fewer and less serious side effects. As more and more published studies confirmed this assessment, SSRI use skyrocketed in both adults and children. Prescriptions for U.S. minors grew annually at double-digit rates through 2003, when 2.4 percent of all American minors—about two million kids—were taking the drugs.

This rise occurred even though no SSRI won FDA approval for use in children until Prozac did in 2003. Once a drug is approved for general use (based on testing in adults), doctors can also prescribe it for children unless a specific ban forbids it. Such "off label" practice is common, legal and, given due care, generally safe. To obtain specific

later the *Journal of the Canadian Medical Association* published a leaked 1998 GlaxoSmithKline memo urging its staff to suppress findings showing that its SSRI, Paxil, worked no better than placebos. Headlines and talk of cover-ups started to fly.

By June, New York State Attorney General Eliot Spitzer had sued Glaxo for consumer fraud, and Glaxo and other companies soon faced both individual and class-action lawsuits from families of children taking SSRIs who had attempted or committed suicide. Finally, September brought that unmistakable certification of scandal, the congressional hearing, where under bright lights both the drug industry and the FDA had to face bipartisan thrashing and wrenching testimony from parents of suicide victims.

The entire episode, as the British medical journal the *Lancet* put it, was "a story of confusion, manipulation, and institutional failure." Fortu-

> Pharmaceutical **companies have cherry-picked data for decades;** only 50 percent of all drug trials over the past half a century were reported or published.

approval for use in children, a pharmaceutical company must run additional trials in pediatric patients.

It was the data from such trials that came to light this summer. In both the U.K. and the U.S., government epidemiologists who ran meta-analyses on the published, positive numbers as well as results from less flattering, previously withheld trials found that overall, SSRIs helped about the same percentage of youths as placebos did, usually a third to a half, depending on the study. Yet the drugs doubled the incidence of suicidal thoughts and tendencies. This reversed the positive benefit-risk balance the companies had shown in their selected studies.

The U.K. responded by banning pediatric use of all SSRIs except Prozac. But when the FDA's epidemiologist, Andrew Mosholder, recommended similarly strong action, the agency deemed his findings inconclusive, ordered another study, forbade him from publishing and blocked him from testifying at FDA hearings on the issue this past February.

Truth wins out, at least sometimes, and the tale of Mosholder's suppressed findings leaked to the press soon after the FDA hearings. A month

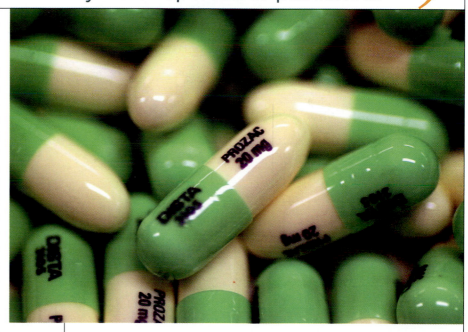

nately, the publicity seems likely to spur a much needed revision of warnings and protocols for pediatric antidepressant use. On the second day of its own September meeting, an FDA advisory committee voted to recommend a "black box" warning for SSRIs—the strongest measure short of a ban. This would require every SSRI container to display a prominent, black-bordered warning about suicide risk on its label and to be dispensed

Prozac prescriptions for children rose for a decade, even though the FDA did not approve this use until 2003.

with a pamphlet describing the risk and urging close monitoring.

The warning would also appear in all ads. Most observers felt this was a good solution, because it would inspire more discretion among doctors, parents and patients while allowing use of SSRIs when needed. Few dispute that the drugs help some patients, sometimes profoundly. And although their use may create suicidal tendencies in some patients, they may prevent needless death

tidepressant prescriptions in the past year. Although doctors worry that wariness will prevent some needy patients from taking the drugs, the warnings should slow what many researchers felt was an overreadiness to prescribe these drugs.

Unfortunately, the deeper problem—a drug approval system that allows industry to highlight flattering results and hide negative ones—will be harder to fix. Drugmakers have cherry-picked their trial data for FDA consideration for decades, defending

the practice in the name of protecting proprietary information; only about 50 percent of all drug trials over the past half a century were reported or published, according to a 2003 study of clinical trials in the *Journal of the American Medical Association* (*JAMA*). As a result, the FDA routinely approves drugs based on partial and often highly unrepresentative data—thereby forcing physicians to rely on the same skewed information.

Given the vast and growing role that medications play in our medical system, critics say that more lives could be in jeopardy. At issue is whether the "science"

Terri Williams of Wetumpka, Ala. (*left*), and friend Rhonda Thrower prepare to speak during an FDA public hearing in February. Williams's son Jacob (*button, photo*) committed suicide at age 14 while taking antidepressants.

in many more. As this story went to press, it was unclear whether the FDA would accept these recommendations, although it usually follows the advice of its advisory committees. Most observers thought the highly publicized recommendations would leave the agency no choice, but others noted that the FDA's chief counsel, Daniel Troy, is a former drug industry lawyer who has often intervened on drug companies' behalf since joining the FDA in 2001.

Hiding Negative Results

If instituted, a black-box warning will almost surely affect SSRI use. The extended controversy may have contributed to a decline in pediatric an-

underlying much of our health care deserves that name. As University of California at San Francisco School of Medicine professor and *JAMA* deputy editor Drummond Rennie puts it, "If a company does 10 trials on a drug, and two show it helps but eight show it works no better than Rice Krispies, I'm not exactly getting a scientific view if they publish only the two positive studies. And this affects me as a patient. I've got a good doctor, and I watch his prescribing hand closely. We like to think we're sophisticated. But how can we practice sophisticated medicine if the drug companies are hiding their results? That's not science. That's marketing."

The solution, Rennie and other expert ob-

> The only fix is to **mandate registration of all drug trials** in a central, public database and to impose heavy fines on companies that do not comply.

EVAN VUCCI AP Photo

servers say, lies in establishing a system that makes all drug trials, not just successful ones, part of the public record. The recent pledges by drug companies to publish their studies in an industry database will not answer the call. Making trial registration voluntary, as the industry wants, still allows the same types of selective publication.

More constructive was the September announcement by 11 major medical journals, including *JAMA*, the *New England Journal of Medicine* and the *Lancet*, that beginning next July, they will require drugmakers to have registered clinical trials at their outset if the companies want the option to eventually publish the results—a move designed to prevent them from hiding studies that don't pan out. Yet this system still allows manip-

from the industry. "Any law establishing a new database has to give the government a big stick," says Kay Dickersin, director of Brown University's Center for Clinical Trials and Evidence-Based Healthcare.

Will it happen? Representatives Edward Markey of Massachusetts and Henry Waxman of California proposed a mandatory trial registration bill in September, and the bipartisan outrage at the congressional hearings suggested its chances were good. But the pharmaceutical industry lobby, one of Washington's most powerful, has resisted this idea for years and will probably oppose the measure vigorously, hoping to satisfy Congress that a voluntary register will suffice. This current Congress is wary of overregulation, and the industry

> At issue is whether the "science" underlying much of our health care deserves that name. **More lives could be in jeopardy.**

ulation unless all the hundreds of existing medical journals observe the policy.

Most doctors and patient advocates say the only sure fix will be to require registration of all drug trials *at their inception* in a central, publicly accessible database that includes a single, unique identifier for each drug, the intended therapeutic use in each trial, and each trial's protocols, outcomes and results. Advocates want a nonprofit or FDA government registry, perhaps building on the existing, voluntary register (available at www.clinicaltrials.gov) that already lists several thousand trials.

If mandatory, such a registry would enable the FDA to easily consider all trial results—whether they are negative, neutral or positive—when weighing a drug's approval. It would also allow physicians and patients to review trial data by drug, and if sufficiently detailed it might allow independent researchers to do meta-analyses of data from multiple trials, providing the kind of vital perspective the British and U.S. government reviews of SSRIs did.

For a registry to work, advocates also say, Congress must not only make trial registrations mandatory but must give the FDA or the Department of Health and Human Services strong enforcement powers, such as extremely punitive fines, to ensure that the drug companies actually register every trial. They note that the one mandatory trial register already in existence, established in 1997 for drugs and devices aimed at life-threatening conditions, gets only 50 percent compliance

claims that providing all trial data jeopardizes proprietary information and competitiveness.

Much depends on the outcome. A well-enforced, mandatory database seems like the only step that can repair the present system's data quality and confidence problems. Anything less is likely to leave both science and confidence wanting.

To trial registration advocates such as *JAMA*'s Rennie and Brown University's Dickersin, there's a painful irony in all this. "We've been pushing trial registration for over two decades," Dickersin says. "But the drug companies have always fended it off by claiming it infringes on their proprietary interests. It's terrible that we had to get to something that involved children and death to make people see the seriousness of this issue. But perhaps this will finally get the job done."

DAVID DOBBS, author of the forthcoming *Reef Madness: Charles Darwin, Alexander Agassiz, and the Meaning of Coral*, writes from Montpelier, Vt.

(Further Reading)
- Andrew Mosholder's originally blocked report urging new curbs on SSRIs may be viewed at www.ahrp.org/risks/SSRImosholder/
- Suppression of Mosholder's findings and testimony is documented by Anna Wilde Mathews's article "In Debate over Antidepressants, FDA Weighed Risk of False Alarm Doubting Data on Suicide and Kids" in *Wall Street Journal*; May 25, 2004. Viewable at www.ahrp.org/infomail/04/05/25.html
- **Drug Company Experts Advised Staff to Withhold Data about SSRI Use in Children.** Wayne Kondro in *Canadian Medical Association Journal*, Vol. 170; No. 5; March 2, 2004. Available online at www.cmaj.ca/cgi/content/full/170/5/783

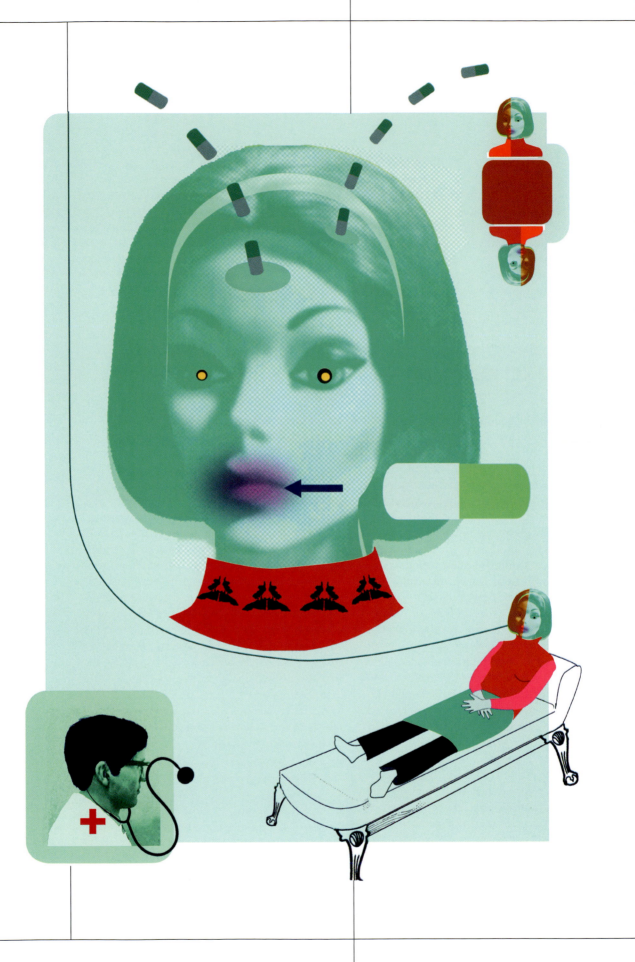

DIGITAL VISION/GETTY IMAGES

Treating Depression: Pills or Talk?

Medication has reduced depression for decades, but newer forms of psychotherapy are proving their worth

BY STEVEN D. HOLLON, MICHAEL E. THASE AND JOHN C. MARKOWITZ

For decades, the public and most mental health professionals have felt that antidepressant medications are a magic bullet for depression. Beginning in the late 1950s, antidepressants ushered in an era of safe, reliable and reasonably affordable treatment that often produced better results than the psychotherapies of the day. As the compounds rose in popularity, many physicians came to view psychotherapy alone as ineffective and as little more than a minor adjunct when combined with medication.

This is no longer the case, if it was ever true. Contrary to prevailing wisdom, recent research suggests that several focused forms of psychotherapy may be as effective as medication, even when treating more severe depressions. Moreover, the newer psychotherapies may provide advantages beyond what antidepressants alone can achieve.

Nevertheless, pharmaceutical therapy remains the current standard of treatment, and effective new options are being added all the time.

These trends are important to examine because depression exacts a significant toll on society as well as individuals. Depression is one of the most common psychiatric disorders and is a leading cause of disability worldwide. The impact of mood disorders on quality of life and economic productivity matches that of heart disease. Depression also accounts for at least half of all suicides.

The efficacy of antidepressants has been established in thousands of placebo-controlled trials. The newer ones are safer and have fewer noxious side effects than earlier compounds. About 50 percent of all patients will respond to any given medication, and many of those who do not will be helped by another agent or a combination of them.

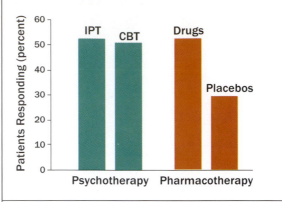

Meta-analysis indicates depression patients respond about equally well to medication or to psychotherapy (interpersonal psychotherapy—IPT—or cognitive and behavioral therapies—CBT).

Not everyone responds, however, and many who do would prefer not to have to take the pills. Quietly over the years, newer psychotherapeutic techniques have been introduced that may be just as good at alleviating acute distress in all but the most severely depressed patients. And some of the therapies provide advantages over medication alone, such as improving the quality of relationships or reducing the risk that symptoms will return after treatment is over.

This last revelation is significant because many people who recover from depression are prone to succumb again. The illness is often chronic, comparable to diabetes or hypertension, and patients treated with medication alone may have to remain on it for years, if not for life, to prevent symptoms from returning. Moreover, combining treatments—prescriptions to reduce acute symptoms quickly and psychotherapy to broaden their effects and to prevent symptoms from returning after treatment terminates—may offer the best chance for a full recovery without recurring problems.

Remission or Relapse

Our conclusions refer mainly to the condition termed unipolar disorder. Depression comes in two basic forms: The unipolar type involves the occurrence of negative moods or loss of interest in daily activities. In the bipolar form, commonly known as manic-depression, patients also experience manic states that may involve euphoria, sleeplessness, grandiosity or recklessness that can lead to everything from buying sprees to impulsive sexual adventures that later bring regret.

Bipolar disorder shows up in only 1 to 2 percent of the population and is usually treated with mood-stabilizing medication such as lithium. In contrast, about 20 percent of women and 10 percent of men suffer from unipolar depression at some time in their lives.

The treatment of unipolar depression typically progresses through three phases, determined by changes in the patient's intensity of symptoms. These are usually measured by clinical ratings such as the Hamilton Rating Scale for Depression. Seriously depressed patients in the acute phase often report feeling down much of the time. They have lost interest in formerly pleasurable activities, and they may have difficulty sleeping, changed appetite, and diminished libido. They may feel fatigued or worthless, and they may entertain recurrent thoughts of death or suicide. The goal of treatment is to relieve symptoms. "Remission" is reached when someone is fully well.

Even when in remission, however, patients may still have an elevated risk for the return of symptoms. It is common practice to encourage patients to stay on medication for at least six months following the initial remission. The return of symptoms soon after remission is called a relapse. In this sense, treating depression with drugs may be like treating an infection with antibiotics; a patient must take the medication beyond the point of first feeling better, to fully prevent the original problem from coming back. This effort to forestall relapse is called continuation treatment and typically lasts at least six to nine months beyond the point of remission.

Those who pass the point at which the treated episode is likely to return are said to have recovered. But even then, they might experience a new episode; people with a history of depression are three to five times more likely to have an episode than those with no such history. A new episode is considered a recurrence. To protect against recurrence, many patients are kept in ongoing maintenance treatment, typically medication but sometimes with psychotherapy. But once patients are off medication, having been on it does nothing to reduce subsequent risk for recurrence. Therefore, patients with a history of multiple episodes are usually advised to stay on medication indefinitely.

Although the scope of depression can vary widely, there are only a few prevailing treatments. Most of the leading antidepressants fall into three main

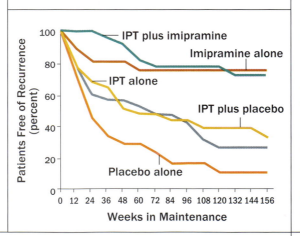

Recovered patients are least likely to suffer new depression if they continue on IPT and imipramine together (*blue*), rather than either treatment alone, according to one study.

(The Antidepressants)

MAOI. Monoamine oxidase inhibitors were the first widely used antidepressants. They curtail the action of an enzyme that breaks down brain neurotransmitters. They are rarely prescribed as a first-line treatment because they require a special diet to avoid potentially dangerous though rare interactions with certain common foods. But they are still a medication of last resort.

TCA. Tricyclic antidepressants inhibit the reuptake of the neurotransmitters norepinephrine and serotonin. TCAs have unpleasant side effects that can include fainting, dry mouth and blurred vision; about 30 percent of patients stop taking the medication because of these problems. TCAs are also potentially lethal in an overdose. But they may still be the medication of choice for those with certain kinds of depression.

SSRI. Selective serotonin reuptake inhibitors, such as Prozac and Paxil, block the reuptake of serotonin back into presynaptic neurons. They have replaced TCAs as the primary medication because they have fewer side effects and are less likely to prove fatal in an overdose. Nevertheless, side effects such as gastrointestinal and sexual problems can be disconcerting. Indications that SSRIs may increase suicidal thoughts and actions in children and teenagers have led to mandatory warnings for these age groups in the U.S. and a ban for minors in Great Britain.

Newer medications. More doctors are trying new drugs that affect multiple neurotransmitter systems or make use of mechanisms other than blocking reuptake. Examples include bupropion, venlafaxine, nefazodone and mirtazapine. —S.H., M.T., J.M.

classes: monoamine oxidase inhibitors (MAOIs), tricyclic antidepressants (TCAs), and selective serotonin reuptake inhibitors (SSRIs), such as Prozac and Paxil [*see box above*]. Each class has a slightly different action and different side effects and is prescribed based on a patient's history, the likelihood of certain complications, and cost. Although about equally effective in a general population, some medications are more efficacious than others for specific types of depression. In general, the older MAOIs and TCAs carry greater risk of side effects than the SSRIs. But the SSRIs do not always work, especially for more severely depressed patients, and they are more expensive.

Despite the widespread use of antidepressants, their actions are not fully understood. They work in part by affecting the neurotransmitters (signaling molecules in the brain) norepinephrine, serotonin and dopamine, which are involved in regulating mood, primarily by blocking the reuptake of these neurotransmitters into the neurons that secrete them. Yet this action cannot fully explain the effects, and it is quite likely that the compounds drive a subsequent cascade of biochemical events. Many people who do not respond to one antidepressant will respond to another or to a combination.

New psychotherapy methods have proved as effective as medication, although they are still not as extensively tested [*see box on next page*]. The programs include interpersonal psychotherapy (IPT), which focuses on problems in relationships and helps patients lift the self-blame common in depression. Developed in the 1970s, IPT has performed well in trials but has only begun to enter clinical practice. Studies do show, however, that when IPT is paired with medication, patients receive the best of both worlds: the quick results of pharmaceutical intervention and greater breadth in improving the quality of their interpersonal lives.

Cognitive and behavioral therapies, collectively known as CBT, also compare well with medication in all but the most severely depressed patients—and they can benefit even those people if they are administered by experienced therapists. Most exciting is that CBT appears to have an enduring effect that reduces risk of relapse and perhaps recurrence. Even the most effective of the other treatments rarely have this type of long-lasting benefit. Cognitive therapy is perhaps the most well established CBT approach. It teaches patients to examine the validity of their dysfunctional depressive beliefs and to alter how they process information about themselves. Behavioral therapy had lost favor to the cognitive approaches, but it, too, has done well in recent trials and is undergoing a revival.

(The Authors)

STEVEN D. HOLLON, MICHAEL E. THASE and **JOHN C. MARKOWITZ** study the treatment and prevention of depression. Hollon is professor of psychology at Vanderbilt University and a past president of the Association for Advancement of Behavior Therapy. Thase is professor of psychiatry at the University of Pittsburgh Medical Center and chief of adult academic psychiatry at the Western Psychiatric Institute and Clinic there. Markowitz is associate professor of psychiatry at Cornell University's Weill Medical College and a research psychiatrist at the New York State Psychiatric Institute.

(Psychotherapies for Depression)

Interpersonal psychotherapy (IPT) focuses on problems in relationships. Therapists help patients to understand life events that may have started their depression and to find ways to combat such episodes as well as reverse cycles of social withdrawal, fatigue and poor concentration. IPT emphasizes that symptoms are the result of a mood disorder and not an outgrowth of personal failure, which lifts the guilt and self-blame common in depression.

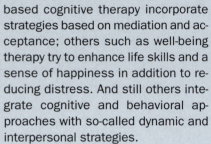

Cognitive and behavior therapies hold that mood disorders are caused or exacerbated by learned beliefs and behaviors—which can be unlearned or modified through experience. The more cognitively based methods emphasize the role of a patient's aberrant beliefs and dysfunctional information processing, whereas the more behavioral approaches focus on how external circumstances shape patient responses. Most therapies blend cognitive and behavioral strategies and are often referred to as CBT. The goal is not to "think happy thoughts" but to become more accurate in one's self-assessments and more effective in one's behaviors. Recent variants such as mindfulness-based cognitive therapy incorporate strategies based on mediation and acceptance; others such as well-being therapy try to enhance life skills and a sense of happiness in addition to reducing distress. And still others integrate cognitive and behavioral approaches with so-called dynamic and interpersonal strategies.

More purely **behavioral therapies** akin to behavioral activation maintain that depression results from too little positive reinforcement, brought on by problems in a person's environment or a lack of social skills or a propensity to avoid challenging situations. These approaches are drawing renewed attention.   —*S.H., M.T., J.M.*

Which Way to Turn

It is not possible to simply say whether medication or psychotherapy is "better" for depressed patients. But many studies have reached interesting conclusions about the approaches when they are applied across the illness's three phases: the acute symptoms at onset, the months of continuation treatment to forestall relapse, and the maintenance of health for years to come.

Among patients who take antidepressants during treatment for acute symptoms, about half show a 50 percent drop in symptom scores on rating tests over the first four to eight weeks. About one third of those patients become fully well (remission). Not all the improvement can be attributed to pharmacology, however. In pill-placebo control experiments, placebos can achieve up to 80 percent of the success rate of active medication, probably by instilling in patients hope and the expectation for change. The placebo effect does tend to be less stable over time and smaller in magnitude in more severe or chronic depressions. A major problem with acute-phase therapy, however, is that many stop taking their medication—primarily because of side effects—before therapists can clearly tell if the agents are working. Attrition rates from clinical trials are often 30 percent or higher for older medications such as the TCAs and around 15 percent for newer options such as the SSRIs.

The newer psychotherapies appear to do as well as medication during the acute depression phase, although the number of studies is fewer and the findings are not always consistent. One typical study found that IPT alone was about as effective as medication alone (with each better than a control condition) and that the combination was better still. In general, medication relieved symptoms more quickly, but IPT produced more improvement in social functioning and quality of relationships. The combined treatment retained the independent benefits of each.

IPT also fared well in the 1989 National Institute of Mental Health Treatment of Depression Collaborative Research Program. The TDCRP, as it is known, is perhaps the most influential study to date that compared medication and psychotherapy. In that trial, patients with major depression were randomly assigned to 16 weeks of IPT, CBT or the TCA imipramine, combined with meetings with a psychiatrist or a placebo plus meetings. Patients with less severe depression improved equally across conditions. Among more severely depressed patients, imipramine worked faster than IPT, but both were comparable by the end of treatment and both were superior to a placebo.

As for CBT, most of the published trials have found it to be as effective as medication in the acute phase. The most notable exception—the TDCRP—did find that cognitive therapy was less efficacious than either medication or IPT (and no better than a placebo) in the treatment of more severely depressed patients. Because the study was large and was the first major comparison to include a pill-placebo control, its results considerably dampened enthusiasm for cognitive therapy, even though no other study had produced such a negative finding.

Today this conclusion appears to have been premature. More recent studies have found that CBT is superior to pill-placebos and is as good as an SSRI for more severely depressed outpatients. These studies suggest that cognitive therapy's success depends greatly on the level of a therapist's training and experience with it, especially for patients with more serious or complicated symptoms.

Continuing the Fight

The best treatments for reducing acute distress also seem to work as well for reducing relapse when they are carried into the continuation phase. Antidepressants appear to reduce the risk for relapse by at least half. It is unclear exactly how long patients must keep taking medication to pass from remission into full recovery, but current convention is to go for at least six to nine months.

IPT during the continuation phase appears to prevent relapse nearly as well as medication, although studies in this regard are few. Recent investigations also suggest that if cognitive therapy is continued past the point of remission, it can reduce the risk for relapse. To date, no studies have compared continuation CBT to continuation IPT or medication.

During the maintenance phase, medication is usually recommended for high-risk patients, especially those with multiple prior episodes. Therapy can go on for years. It does protect against recurrence. Even among recovered patients, though, the risk of recurrence off medication is at least two to three times greater. Given that there is no evidence that prior medication use does anything to reduce subsequent risk for recurrence, most physicians will encourage their high-risk patients to stay on medication indefinitely.

Studies of maintenance IPT are few, but they generally support the notion that it, too, reduces risk of recurrence. It has not been as efficacious as keeping people on medication, but the handful of studies have typically cut back the frequency of IPT to monthly sessions while maintaining medication at full, acute-treatment dosages. It would be interesting to see how maintenance IPT compares when the psychotherapy sessions are also kept at "full strength."

Several studies have shown that CBT has an enduring protective benefit that extends beyond the end of treatment. Patients treated to remission with CBT were only about half as likely to relapse after treatment termination as patients treated to remission with medication, and the CBT patients were no

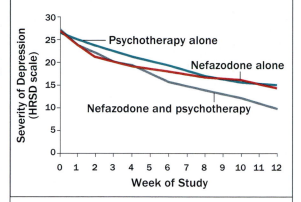

Combining medication (nefazodone) and psychotherapy (*gray*) reduced the intensity of symptoms furthest among chronically depressed patients in a 2000 study.

more likely to relapse than patients who continued on the prescriptions. CBT appears to produce this enduring effect regardless of whether it is provided alone or in combination with medication during acute treatment and even if it is added only after medication has reduced acute symptoms. Further, indications are that this enduring effect may even prevent wholly new episodes (recurrence), although findings are still far from conclusive.

Given these trends, CBT may ultimately prove more cost-effective than medication. Psychotherapy usually costs at least twice as much as medication over the first several months, but if the enduring effect of CBT truly extends over time, it may prove less costly for patients to learn the skills involved and discontinue treatment than to stay on medication indefinitely. It remains unclear whether other interventions such as IPT have an enduring effect, but this possibility should certainly be explored.

Our review of the treatment literature indicates that some forms of psychotherapy can work as well as medication in alleviating acute distress. IPT may enhance the breadth of response, and CBT may enhance its stability. Combined treatment, though more costly, appears to retain the advantages of each approach. Good medical care can be hard to find, and the psychotherapies that have garnered the most empirical support are still not widely practiced. Nevertheless, some kind of treatment is almost always better than none for a person facing depression. The real tragedy is that even as alternatives expand, too few people seek help.

(Further Reading)

◆ Three-Year Outcomes for Maintenance Therapies in Recurrent Depression. E. Frank et al. in *Archives of General Psychiatry,* Vol. 47, No. 12, pages 1093–1099; December 1990.

◆ A Comparison of Nefazodone, the Cognitive Behavioral-Analysis System of Psychotherapy, and Their Combination for the Treatment of Chronic Depression. M. B. Keller et al. in *New England Journal of Medicine,* Vol. 342, No. 20, pages 1462–1470; May 18, 2000.

◆ Treatment and Prevention of Depression. Steven Hollon, Michael Thase and John Markowitz in *Psychological Science in the Public Interest,* Vol. 3, No. 2, pages 39–77; November 2002.

DIAGNOSING DISORDERS

PSYCHIATRIC ILLNESSES ARE OFTEN HARD TO RECOGNIZE, BUT GENETIC TESTING AND NEUROIMAGING COULD SOMEDAY BE USED TO IMPROVE DETECTION   BY STEVEN E. HYMAN

MELISSA SZALKOWSKI

ACCURATE DIAGNOSIS IS THE CORNERSTONE OF medical care. To plan a successful treatment for a patient, a doctor must first determine the nature of the illness. In most branches of medicine, physicians can base their diagnoses on objective tests: a doctor can examine x-rays to see if a bone is broken, for example, or extract tissue samples to search for cancer cells. But for some common and serious psychiatric disorders, diagnoses are still based entirely on the patient's own report of symptoms and the doctor's observations of the patient's behavior. The human brain is so enormously complex that medical researchers have not yet been able to devise definitive tests to diagnose illnesses such as schizophrenia, autism, bipolar disorder or major depression.

Because psychiatrists must employ subjective evaluations, they face the challenge of reliability: how to ensure that two different doctors arrive at the same diagnosis for the same patient. To address this concern, the American Psychiatric Association in 1980 published the Diagnostic and Statistical Manual of Mental Disorders, Third Edition (widely known by the acronym "DSM-III"). Unlike ear-

lier editions of the manual, DSM-III and its successor volumes (the latest one is referred to as DSM-IV-TR) describe what symptoms must be present—and for how long—to make a diagnosis of a particular brain disorder. Virtually all these criteria, however, are based on the patient's history and the clinical encounter. Without the ability to apply objective tests, physicians may fail to detect disorders and sometimes mistake the symptoms of one illness for another's. Making the task more difficult is the fact that some psychiatric illnesses, such as schizophrenia, may turn out to be clusters of diseases that have similar symptoms but require different treatments.

In recent years, though, advances in genetics, brain imaging and basic neuroscience have promised to change the way that brain disorders are diagnosed. By correlating variations in DNA with disease risks, researchers may someday be able to determine which small differences in a patient's genetic sequence can make that person more vulnerable to schizophrenia, autism or other illnesses. And rapid developments in neuroimaging—the noninvasive observation of a liv-

Brain disorders usually have behavioral symptoms that can be observed by a psychiatrist. But the checklist approach to diagnosis is far from perfect.

ing brain—may eventually enable doctors to spot structural features or patterns of brain activity that are characteristic of certain disorders. Better diagnosis will lead to better care: after pinpointing a patient's brain disorder, a physician will be able to prescribe the treatment that is best suited to it. And earlier diagnosis could allow doctors to slow or halt the progress of a disorder before it becomes debilitating.

History of Diagnosis

THE FIRST MODERN ATTEMPT to identify individual psychiatric disorders was made in the 19th century by German scientist Emil Kraepelin, who distinguished two of the most severe mental illnesses: schizophrenia, which he called dementia praecox, and manic-depressive illness, which is now known as bipolar disorder. Much of his careful observational work focused on following the course of the illnesses over the lifetime of his patients. He defined schizophrenia as a disease with psychotic

failure to successfully negotiate stages in psychological development. The symptoms of each illness indicated the point in development at which the trouble arose. The psychoanalytic theory of that period did not allow for the possibility that different psychiatric illnesses might have completely different causes, let alone the modern idea that mental disorders might arise from abnormalities in brain circuits.

Diagnosis returned to a central position in psychiatry in the 1950s, though, with the discovery of drugs for treating psychiatric disorders. Researchers found that chlorpromazine (better known by one of its brand names, Thorazine) could control the psychotic symptoms of schizophrenia and that lithium salts could stabilize the moods of patients with bipolar disorder. By 1960 the first antidepressant and antianxiety drugs were introduced. It quickly became critically important to match the patient with the right treatment. The new antidepressants did not work for schizophrenia and could precipi-

Some PSYCHIATRIC ILLNESSES may turn out to be clusters of diseases that have similar symptoms but REQUIRE DIFFERENT TREATMENTS.

symptoms (such as hallucinations and delusions) that had an insidious onset—in other words, the initial symptoms may be hard to detect—and a chronic, downhill course. In contrast, manic-depressive illness was characterized by discrete episodes of illness alternating with periods of relatively healthy mental function.

In the early 20th century, however, work on psychiatric diagnosis went into eclipse as a result of the influence of the psychoanalytic theories developed by Sigmund Freud and his followers. In their conception of mental illness, symptoms arose from a

tate an episode of mania in someone with bipolar disorder. Lithium was remarkably effective for bipolar disorder but not for schizophrenia.

In the 1980s the publication of DSM-III and subsequent manuals enabled psychiatrists to use standardized interviews and checklists of symptoms to make their diagnoses. Although the checklist approach is imperfect, it represented an enormous advance in both clinical care and research. For example, before the advent of DSM-III, it appeared that schizophrenia was twice as prevalent in the U.S. as it was in Great Britain. This discrepancy turned out to be an artifact of divergent approaches to diagnosis. In fact, the prevalence of schizophrenia is about 1 percent of people worldwide. The standardization of diagnosis made it clear that mental disorders are common and quite often disabling. According to the World Health Organization's data on the global burden of disease, major depression is the leading cause of disability in the U.S. and other economically advanced nations. In aggregate, mental disorders rank second only to cardiovascular diseases in terms of their economic and social costs in those countries.

Meanwhile advances in neuroscience showed that certain neurological diseases leave unmistakable signatures on the brain. Parkinson's disease,

OVERVIEW/*Improving Diagnosis*

- Because psychiatrists lack objective tests for detecting brain disorders, they sometimes fail to observe mental illness or mistake the symptoms of one disorder for another's.
- Scientists have recently found gene variants that seem to confer susceptibility to disorders such as schizophrenia and autism. Doctors may someday be able to determine a patient's risk of developing these diseases by analyzing his or her DNA.
- In addition, advances in neuroimaging may allow physicians to look for subtle anomalies in the brain caused by mental disorders. As the technology improves, doctors could use neuroimaging to diagnose psychiatric illnesses and to track the success of therapy.

for instance, is characterized by the death of nerve cells in the midbrain that make the neurotransmitter dopamine, a chemical that transmits signals between neurons. The definitive signs of Alzheimer's disease are deposits of an abnormal protein called amyloid and tangles of protein in the cells of the cerebral cortex, the outermost layer of the brain. (Because one needs a microscope to observe these anomalies, a conclusive diagnosis can be made only after the patient's death.) But when it comes to psychiatric illnesses such as schizophrenia and depression, the abnormalities in the brain are much more subtle and difficult to discover. For this reason, many researchers have begun to look for indicators of brain disorders in the human genome.

The Genetics of Disorder

JUST AS NORMAL behavioral traits are often passed from parent to child, certain mental disorders run in families. To determine whether the resemblance is a result of genes or family environment, researchers have conducted studies comparing the risk of illness in identical twins (who share 100 percent of their DNA) to the risk in fraternal twins (who on average share 50 percent of their DNA). Another type of study, which is more cumbersome, focuses on whether an illness in offspring who were adopted early in life is more often shared with their biological relatives or their adoptive families.

Such studies reveal that genes play a substantial role in the transmission of mental disorders but that other factors must also be at work. For example, if one identical twin has schizophrenia, the risk to the other is 45 percent. If one identical twin has autism—a developmental brain disorder characterized by impairments in communication and social interaction—the other twin has a 60 percent chance of sharing the same diagnosis. These are enormous increases over the risks for the general population (1 percent for schizophrenia, 0.2 percent for autism), but the key point here is that some twins do not develop the disorders even if they carry the same genes as their affected siblings.

Therefore, nongenetic factors must also contribute to the risk of illness. These factors may include environmental influences (such as infections or injuries to the brain early in life) and the random twists and turns of brain development. Even among identical twins growing up in exactly the same environment, it is not possible to wire up a brain with 100 trillion synapses in identical fashion. For all mental disorders—and, indeed, for all normal patterns of behavior that have been studied—genes are important, but they are not equivalent to fate. Our brains, not our genes, directly regulate our behav-

GENE CHIP IMAGE COURTESY OF AFFYMETRIX; SOURCE FOR CHART: NATIONAL ACADEMY OF SCIENCES

FIRST STEPS TOWARD A GENETIC TEST?

PEOPLE WHO POSSESS DNA SEQUENCE VARIATIONS in any of the four genes shown below appear to have a slightly increased risk of developing schizophrenia. These genes are involved in the transmission of signals among neurons in the brain, so it is possible that the genetic variations disrupt that process. But possessing the variations is neither necessary nor sufficient to cause schizophrenia, which most likely arises by several pathways. In the future, as researchers learn more about the genetic and nongenetic causes of brain disorders, doctors may be able to estimate a patient's risk of acquiring a psychiatric illness by analyzing his or her DNA with a gene chip (*at right*).

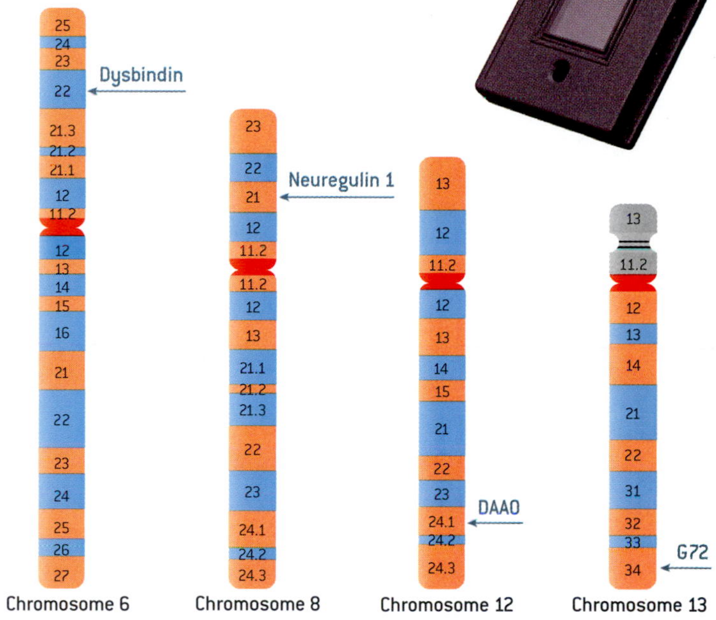

Dysbindin — Chromosome 6
Neuregulin 1 — Chromosome 8
DAAO — Chromosome 12
G72 — Chromosome 13

ior, and our brains are the products of genes, environment and chance operating over a lifetime.

What is more, new research indicates that the strong genetic influence on the risk of developing a disorder such as schizophrenia is not the work of a single gene. Rather, the increase in risk seems to be an aggregate effect of many genes interacting with one another and with nongenetic factors. By studying the DNA sequences of people with schizophre-

THE AUTHOR

From an early age, *STEVEN E. HYMAN* was curious about how our brains underlie thinking, emotion and behavioral control. He studied philosophy as an undergraduate at Yale University and philosophy of science at the University of Cambridge, where he was a Mellon Fellow. After earning his M.D. at Harvard University, he received clinical training in psychiatry and scientific training in molecular neurobiology. He was the founding director of Harvard's Interfaculty Initiative in Mind, Brain and Behavior. From 1996 to 2001 he served as Director of the National Institute of Mental Health, the component of the National Institutes of Health charged with generating the knowledge needed to understand, treat and prevent mental illness. Since 2001 he has been Harvard's provost and a professor of neurobiology at Harvard Medical School.

nia and their family members, researchers have already found several genetic variations that appear to increase susceptibility to the disorder [*see illustration on preceding page*]. These variations occur in genes that code proteins involved in the transmission of signals among neurons in the brain, so it is possible that the variations disrupt that process. Similar studies have identified genetic variations that appear to increase the risk of developing major depression and bipolar disorder. Furthermore, a variation of *HOXA1,* a gene related to early brain development, seems to boost susceptibility to autism. The variant gene is present in about 20 percent of the general population but in about 40 percent of people with autism.

Although possessing the variation of *HOXA1* approximately doubles the risk of developing autism, more than 99.5 percent of people who have the variant gene do not acquire the disorder, and about 60 percent of people with autism do not possess the variant gene. As is the case for many diseases, there is not likely to be a single set of genes

arrays of thousands of reference DNA samples—researchers can also discover which genes are actively coding proteins in a given cell or tissue.

If the gene-hunting effort is successful, doctors will someday be able to analyze a patient's genetic sequence and see where it fits in the matrix of risks. The accuracy of this matrix would be greatly enhanced if physicians also had more information about environmental risk factors. In all likelihood, none of the environmental influences has an overwhelming effect on illness risk—otherwise, researchers would have probably noticed it by now—so epidemiologists will need to study large numbers of people to tease out all the small contributions. By taking both genetic and environmental factors into account, this method may be able to determine whether a person is at high risk for acquiring a particular brain disorder. High-risk patients could then receive close scrutiny in follow-up observations, and if symptoms of the disorder appear, doctors would be able to begin treatment at the earliest stages of the illness.

Genes are not equivalent to fate. Our brains are the PRODUCTS OF GENES, ENVIRONMENT AND CHANCE operating over a lifetime.

that are necessary and sufficient to cause either schizophrenia or autism. Instead these illnesses may arise by several pathways. This situation, called genetic complexity, seems to apply to bipolar disorder and depression as well. Each of these disorders may actually represent a group of closely related mental illnesses that share key aspects of abnormal physiology and symptoms but may differ in details large and small, including severity and responsiveness to treatment.

What are the implications for diagnosis? Imagine that variations in 10 distinct genes can boost the risk of developing a mental illness but that none of the genetic variations by itself is either necessary or sufficient to bring on the disorder (this is close to a current model for autism). Different combinations of the variant genes may confer risks of similar but not identical forms of the illness. To correlate all the possible genetic combinations with all the clinical outcomes would be an immensely complex task. But the tools for such an undertaking are already available. Thanks to technologies developed for the Human Genome Project, scientists can rapidly determine what variations are present in a person's DNA. Using gene chips—small glass slides holding

For patients already showing symptoms of a disorder, their genetic information would be quite useful in narrowing down the diagnostic possibilities. And as researchers learn how genetic variations can affect responses to drugs, knowing a patient's genomic profile could help a physician choose the best treatment. But there is a downside to this medical advance: in a society where people can carry their DNA sequences on a memory chip, policymakers would have to grapple with the question of who should have access to this data. Even though a genetic sequence by itself cannot definitively predict whether a person will descend into depression or psychosis, one can readily imagine how employers, educational institutions and insurance companies might use or misuse this information. Society at large will have to become far more sophisticated in its interpretation of the genetic code.

Imaging the Brain

MOVING IN PARALLEL with the genomic revolution, neuroscientists have dramatically improved their ability to image the living brain noninvasively. There are three major types of neuroimaging studies. The first is morphometric analysis, which

TELLTALE SIGNS IN THE BRAIN

THREE-DIMENSIONAL MAPS of the brain derived from magnetic resonance imaging reveal that one type of schizophrenia causes a characteristic pattern of tissue loss in the cerebral cortex. The maps show that the average annual reduction in the cortical gray matter of adolescent patients suffering from childhood-onset schizophrenia (*right*) is much greater than the loss in healthy teenagers (*left*) between the ages of 13 and 18.

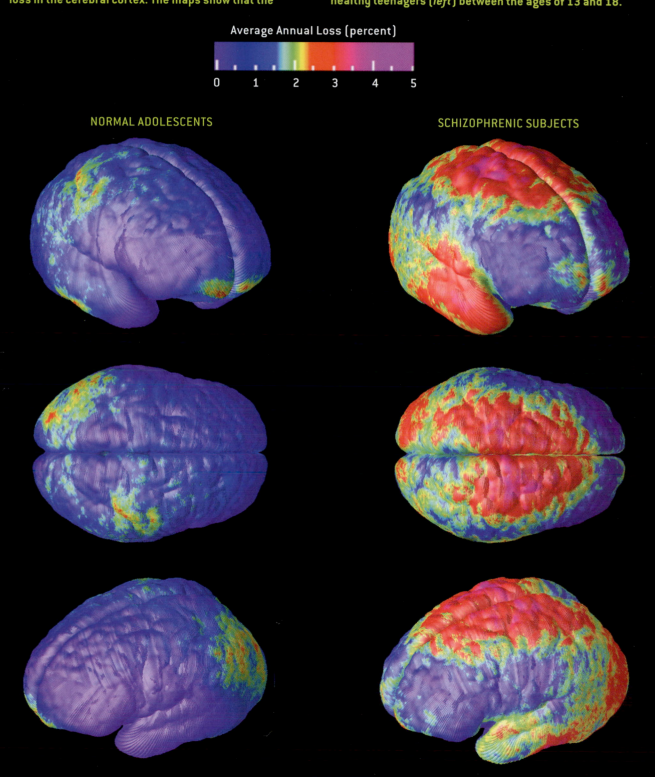

Average Annual Loss (percent)

0 1 2 3 4 5

NORMAL ADOLESCENTS

SCHIZOPHRENIC SUBJECTS

COURTESY OF PAUL THOMPSON AND ARTHUR W. TOGA *UCLA Laboratory of Neuro Imaging* AND JUDITH L. RAPOPORT *National Institute of Mental Health*

THE SPECTRUM OF PSYCHIATRIC ILLNESS

MENTAL DISORDERS, which afflict millions of people every year, can be hard to diagnose. As the table shows, some illnesses have overlapping symptoms. Certain mood disorders, such as major depression and dysthymia, have similar symptoms but differ in severity. Among anxiety disorders, the primary distinction is the trigger that initiates fear, panic or avoidance behavior. Psychotic disorders also range from mild to severe. More definitive diagnostic methods are clearly needed.

DISORDER	COMMON SYMPTOMS	PREVALENCE (PERCENT)*
MOOD DISORDERS		
Major Depression	Characterized by episodes during which the patient feels sad or empty nearly every day; loses interest or pleasure in hobbies and activities; experiences changes in appetite, weight, energy levels or sleeping patterns; or harbors thoughts of death or suicide	5.3
Dysthymia	Similar to major depression, but the symptoms are less severe and more chronic. Sad or empty mood on most days for at least two years. Other symptoms include low self-esteem, fatigue and poor concentration.	1.6
Bipolar I	Episodes of abnormally elevated or irritable mood during which the patient feels inflated self-esteem; needs less sleep; talks more than usual; or engages excessively in pleasurable but unwise activities. These manic periods may alternate with depressive episodes	1.1
Bipolar II	Depressive episodes alternate with less severe manic periods that do not markedly impair functioning or require hospitalization	0.6
ANXIETY DISORDERS		
Specific Phobia	Excessive or unreasonable fear of a specific object or situation, such as flying, heights, animals, receiving an injection or seeing blood. Exposure to the stimulus may provoke a panic attack (palpitations, sweating, trembling, shortness of breath, etc.)	8.3
Agoraphobia	Anxiety about being in any place or situation from which escape might be difficult. Typical fears involve being alone outside the home, standing in a crowd, crossing a bridge, or traveling in a bus, train or automobile	4.9
Post-traumatic Stress Disorder	Patient persistently reexperiences a traumatic event through distressing recollections, recurring dreams or intense reactions to anything symbolizing or resembling the event	3.6
PSYCHOTIC DISORDERS		
Schizophrenia	Characterized by delusions, hallucinations, disorganized speech, inappropriate or blunted emotional responses, loss of motivation and cognitive deficits	1.3
Schizophreniform Disorder	Similar to schizophrenia, but the symptoms last for less than six months and may not be severe enough to impair social or occupational functioning	0.1

Percent of U.S. population between ages 18 and 54 suffering from the disorder in any one-year period.

generally relies on high-resolution magnetic resonance imaging (MRI) to produce precise measurements of brain structures. The second is functional neuroimaging, which generates maps of brain activity by detecting signals that correlate with the firing of brain cells. Functional neuroimaging usually involves the application of MRI or positron emission tomography (PET). The third type of neuroimaging, which typically employs PET, uses radioactive tracers to locate and quantify specific molecules in the brain. In research settings, imaging tools can help explain what goes wrong in the brain to produce certain mental illnesses, and these findings in turn can help define the boundaries of brain disorders. In clinical settings, neuroimaging tools may eventually play a role in diagnosis and in monitoring the effectiveness of treatment.

To be useful for psychiatric diagnosis, a test based on neuroimaging must be affordable and feasible to administer. It must also be sensitive enough to detect the inconspicuous features of a particular brain disorder and yet specific enough to rule out other conditions. Some anatomical signs of mental disorders are nonspecific: people with schizophrenia generally have enlarged cerebral ventricles (the fluid-filled spaces deep in the brain), but this abnormality may also occur in people with alcoholism or Alzheimer's. In patients with severe, chronic depression, the hippocampus—a brain structure critically involved in memory—may be atrophied, but

SOURCES: NATIONAL INSTITUTE OF MENTAL HEALTH; *DIAGNOSTIC AND STATISTICAL MANUAL OF MENTAL DISORDERS, FOURTH EDITION,* 1994